A/AS LEVEL MATHEMATICS

S 1
REVISION WORKBOOK
Version O

Introduction

This workbook is designed to be used as a revision tool as you prepare for your Module S1 examination.
It consists of:

>*revision notes*
>*formulae*
>*examples for you to complete*
>*practice questions.*

We suggest you write in this book in pencil. There should be plenty of room in the example and answer boxes for your answers, but you can correct your work if necessary if you have used pencil. There are hints in the right hand column of some problems which you can cover up if you wish to complete the problems unaided.
There are suggested solutions in the answers section at the back of the book.
Do not think you can work through this book in one attempt. It will be far more useful to attempt one section at a time and ensure you have all the rules and methods secure before attempting the next section.

You should use this workbook in conjunction with past module papers and consult with your Mathematics tutor to revise effectively.

P. Thorns

Alpha Workbooks

Published by Alpha Workbooks.
Tel: 01206 522543
www.alphaworkbooks.com
phil@alphaworkbooks.com

Contents

ISBN　　: 978 1 903406 45 8

PRESENTING DATA

Qualitative data:

This is non-numerical data. For example the colour of cars, type of crop grown or type of career. Suitable diagrams to show the numbers in each group would be bar charts, sectional bar charts, dual bar charts or pie charts.

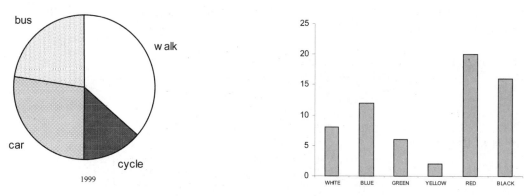

Numerical data:

Data based on numbers are called numerical data. For example lengths, weights, time, score

Discrete Data can only take particular values e.g. number of tables, shoe size, goals scored.
A suitable diagram to show the numbers for each value would be a vertical line chart.

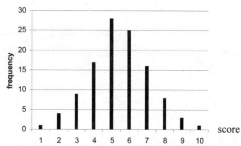

Continuous data can take any values e.g. height of a child, length of a room, temperature in a room.
A suitable diagram to show the distribution of the values would be a histogram.
Here is a histogram to represent some data:

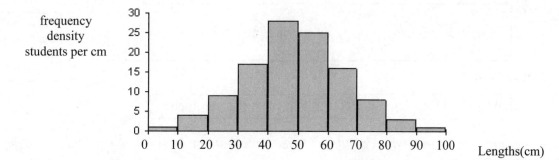

Joining the midpoints of the tops of the bars of the histogram gives a **frequency polygon**. Normally the bars would not be displayed on the same diagram.

Describing the shape of a distribution:

From the above diagram of the distribution of lengths we get an idea of the overall 'shape' of the distribution and describe the different types as follows:

symmetrical

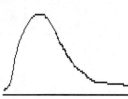
positive skew

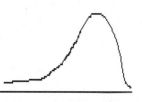
negative skew

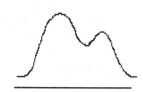
bimodal

WORKING WITH RAW DATA

Measures of central tendency:

Mode: this is the value that occurs most often.

Median: this is the middle value once the data have been arranged in order. If there are two numbers in the middle add them up and divide by two.

Mean: add up all the values and divide by the number of values.

$$\bar{x} = \frac{\sum x}{n}$$

Measures of dispersion:

Range:

Range = highest value - lowest value

Interquartile Range:

Interquartile Range = Upper Quartile - Lower Quartile

If the data set is small you can usually work out the Quartiles by inspection.

For 20 data items the median is the mean of the 10th and 11th values.

The lower quartile is then the middle of the lower half of values i.e. the mean of the 5th and 6th values
The upper quartile is then the middle of the upper half of values i.e. the mean of the 15th and 16th values

1st 2nd 3rd 4th 5th 6th 7th 8th 9th 10th 11th 12th 13th 14th 15th 16th 17th 18th 19th 20th

↑   ↑   ↑
lower quartile   median   upper quartile

For large n, use ¼ n , ½ n and ¾ n to find the lower quartile, median and upper quartile respectively.

Variance:

$$\text{variance} = \frac{\sum (x - \bar{x})^2}{n} \quad \text{or} \quad \text{variance} = \frac{\sum x^2}{n} - \bar{x}^2$$

The second formula is usually easier to set out and use.

Standard Deviation:

Standard Deviation is the square root of the variance

LEARN THESE - They are **not** in formula book

When entering data values into your calculator make sure that you know which symbols give the required statistic (there are various similar symbols)

1. For the following set of data find the mean and standard deviation. 3, 5, 7, 9. $\bar{x} = \dfrac{+\quad +\quad +}{\quad} =$ $\text{variance} = \dfrac{+\quad +\quad +}{\quad} -$ $\text{standard deviation} = \sqrt{\quad} =$	Could just use your calculator! Here show working and check answer using calculator. Add up the values and divide by the number of values. Using the easier form. The variance --- 'the mean of the squares minus the square of the mean' (square the values, add them up and divide by the number of values i.e. 4 Then subtract the mean squared.) Square root for standard deviation.

2. Find the mean and standard deviation of 22, 21, 16, 17, 17, 22, 19, 16, 15, 15, 19, 21, 22, 16, 20, 14, 22, 17, 16, 18

3. For a particular population of 20 numbers

$$\sum x = 184 \quad \text{and} \quad \sum x^2 = 2648$$

Find the mean and standard deviation.

$$\bar{x} = \frac{\sum x}{n} = \underline{\hspace{3cm}} =$$

$$\text{variance} = \frac{\sum x^2}{n} - \bar{x}^2 =$$

$$\text{standard deviation} = \sqrt{\underline{\hspace{2cm}}} =$$

Sometimes you are given questions in this form. So you need to be able to use the particular formulae that include $\sum x$ and $\sum x^2$

Answers 9.2, 6.91

4. The heights, h, of 9 plants were found to have a mean of 12cm and a standard deviation of 2.

(i) Find $\sum h$ and $\sum h^2$

(ii) An additional plant has a height of 2 cm. Find the mean and standard deviation of all 10 plants.

Use the formulae to work out $\sum h$ and $\sum h^2$. Then add in the new number and the new number squared respectively. Then use the formulae to work out the new mean and s.d.

Using your calculator - *When entering data values into your calculator make sure that you know which symbols give the required statistic (there are various similar symbols).*

Enter the following as data items/list and hence find the mean and standard deviation either direct from your calculator or by obtaining Σx, Σy etc. and using the formula.

Do not just write down two numbers. Write mean or $\bar{x} =$ and standard deviation =

If you incorrectly round a number you may lose all marks having shown no working. You should write down you calculator value to say six significant figures and then round to 3 significant figures or how many figures or decimal places you are told.

5. Find the mean and standard deviation of the following

a) 5.6, 6.9, 8.5, 6.1

b) 24, 35, 67, 25, 36, 62, 21, 13, 0, 54

c) 568, 691, 999, 541, 853

Stem-and-leaf diagrams:

Stem-and-leaf diagrams are a useful way of grouping data into classes without losing the values of the individual items of data.

REMEMBER: CLASS INTERVALS MUST BE EQUAL
                            A KEY IS ESSENTIAL

It is usual to draw an unsorted diagram first, just allocating each LEAF of data to its appropriate STEM. Then the leaves can be sorted into order for the final diagram.

EXAMPLE

The times taken by 21 students to swim one length of a pool are 22, 21, 16, 17, 17, 22, 19, 16, 15, 15, 19, 21, 22, 16, 20, 14, 22, 17, 16, 18 and 21 seconds, correct to the nearest second. Complete the unsorted stem-and-leaf diagram for this data.
Use class intervals 14-15, 16-17, 18-19, …

The first four numbers in the list have been written in.
The lowest class is 14-15
The next one up is 16-17 and so on.

Smallest groups at the top and work down.

Stem	Leaf
1	
1	6 7
1	
2	1
2	2

KEY
2 | 1 represents
21 seconds

Make sure you line the numbers up vertically as well as horizontally

Now rearrange the leaves to produce a sorted diagram

1	
1	
1	
2	0 1 1 1
2	2 2 2 2

KEY
2 | 1 represents
21 seconds

The smaller leaves in each interval lie next to the stem.
The largest 8 data values have been written in.

This diagram should give you a lot of information easily.
COMPLETE THE FOLLOWING
1) The quickest swimmer took ____ seconds
2) The slowest swimmer took ____ seconds
3) The modal group is those students who took ____ seconds
4) The range of times for these swimmers is ____ seconds
5) The median (or middle) value is the time taken by the eleventh swimmer once the times are in sorted order.
    The median time is ____ seconds

Median:
21 students - 11th gives the median
Start at the top of the diagram and count through the times, in order, until the 11th is reached. For each interval start at the stem edge and count outwards. 14, 15, 15, 16, 16, 16, ……
(If you start at the bottom you must count from the outside in!)

Stem-and-leaf diagram of the ages of members of a Golf Club and a Squash Club

SQUASH   **GOLF**

	Stem	
9 8 8 7	**10**	
9 8 7 7 4 3 3 2 1 1 1	**20**	
6 6 6 6 5 5 4 3 2 2 1 0 0	**30**	
4 4 3 2 2 0 0	**40**	
7 2	**50**	
2	**60**	

Key: 1 | 20
represents 21

Key:
represents

The ages of the golfers are 18, 23, 25, 29, 34, 36, 36, 38, 38, 40, 41, 42, 42, 43, 44, 45, 45, 46, 47, 47, 49, 50, 50, 52, 52, 54, 54, 56, 56, 56, 57, 58, 58, 59, 60, 60, 61, 62   Add them to the diagram
Complete:
SQUASH PLAYERS

    The mode =   The median =   (careful - not 35, 35.5 or 36)

    Lower quartile =   Upper quartile =   (see previous section if you are not sure about quartiles)

    Interquartile range =

Describe "the shape" of the distribution of the ages of the squash players.

GOLF PLAYERS
    The mode =   The median =   (careful - not 41, 41.5 or 42)

    Lower quartile =   Upper quartile =

    Interquartile range =

Describe "the shape" of the distribution of the ages of the golf players.

Coding:

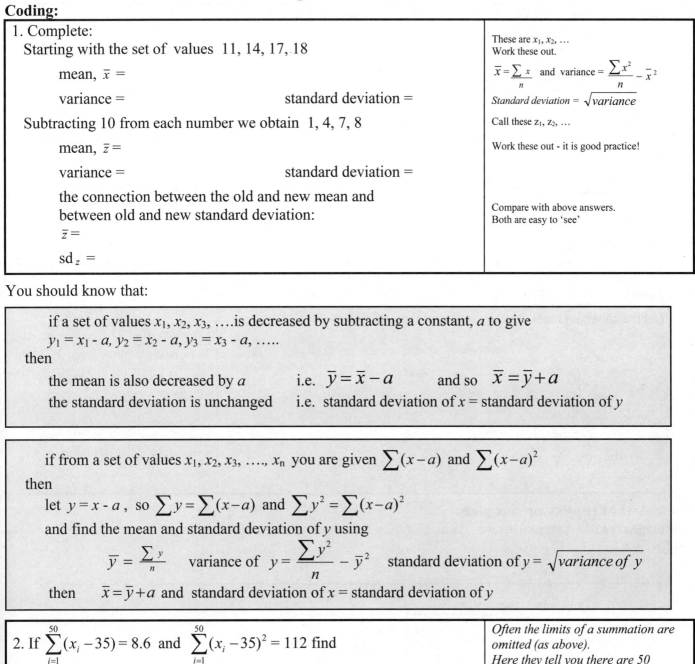

1. Complete:

Starting with the set of values 11, 14, 17, 18

These are $x_1, x_2, \ldots$
Work these out.

mean, $\bar{x} =$

$$\bar{x} = \frac{\sum x}{n} \quad \text{and} \quad \text{variance} = \frac{\sum x^2}{n} - \bar{x}^2$$

variance =   standard deviation =

Standard deviation = $\sqrt{variance}$

Subtracting 10 from each number we obtain 1, 4, 7, 8

Call these $z_1, z_2, \ldots$

mean, $\bar{z} =$

Work these out - it is good practice!

variance =   standard deviation =

the connection between the old and new mean and between old and new standard deviation:

Compare with above answers.
Both are easy to 'see'

$\bar{z} =$

$\text{sd}_z =$

You should know that:

if a set of values $x_1, x_2, x_3, \ldots$ is decreased by subtracting a constant, a to give
$y_1 = x_1 - a, \; y_2 = x_2 - a, \; y_3 = x_3 - a, \ldots$
then

the mean is also decreased by a i.e. $\bar{y} = \bar{x} - a$ and so $\bar{x} = \bar{y} + a$

the standard deviation is unchanged   i.e. standard deviation of x = standard deviation of y

if from a set of values $x_1, x_2, x_3, \ldots, x_n$ you are given $\sum (x - a)$ and $\sum (x - a)^2$
then

let $y = x - a$, so $\sum y = \sum (x - a)$ and $\sum y^2 = \sum (x - a)^2$

and find the mean and standard deviation of y using

$$\bar{y} = \frac{\sum y}{n} \quad \text{variance of } y = \frac{\sum y^2}{n} - \bar{y}^2 \quad \text{standard deviation of } y = \sqrt{variance \; of \; y}$$

then $\bar{x} = \bar{y} + a$ and standard deviation of x = standard deviation of y

2. If $\displaystyle\sum_{i=1}^{50} (x_i - 35) = 8.6$ and $\displaystyle\sum_{i=1}^{50} (x_i - 35)^2 = 112$ find

Often the limits of a summation are omitted (as above).
Here they tell you there are 50 x values.

i) $\bar{x}$ (ii) the standard deviation of x (iii) $\displaystyle\sum_{i=1}^{50} x_i$ (iv) $\displaystyle\sum_{i=1}^{50} x_i^2$

i) let $y = x - 35$, so $\sum y = 8.6$ and $\sum y^2 = 112$

$$\bar{y} = \frac{\sum y}{n} = \qquad\qquad \text{then} \qquad \bar{x} = \bar{y} + a =$$

Find the mean of y and add 35 to find the mean of x.

ii) variance of $y = \dfrac{\sum y^2}{n} - \bar{y}^2 =$

standard deviation of $y = \sqrt{\rule{3cm}{0pt}}$

standard deviation of x = standard deviation of $y =$

Find the variance and hence the standard deviation of y. This is the same as the standard deviation of x.

iii) $\displaystyle\sum_{i=1}^{50} x_i =$

$\bar{x} = \frac{\sum x}{n}$ Hence find $\sum x$.

iv)   variance of $x =$

Square standard deviation of x to obtain the variance of x then use
var of $x = \frac{\sum x^2}{n} - \bar{x}^2$ fo find $\sum x^2$

3. The times taken, t seconds, by 20 students to complete a task are summarised by the equations
$$\sum(t-180) = 540 \text{ and } \sum(t-180)^2 = 16025$$
Find the mean and standard deviation of the times taken to complete the task.

  let $y = t - 180$, so $\sum y =$ and $\sum y^2 =$

  $\bar{y} =$ then   mean time, $\bar{t} =$

        variance of $y =$

  standard deviation of $y =$

  standard deviation of $t =$

Find the mean of y and add 180 to find the mean of t.

Find the variance and hence the standard deviation of y. This is the same as the standard deviation of t.

4. The weights, x g, of 10 fish caught from a lake are summarised by the equations $\sum(x-400) = 840 \text{ and } \sum(x-400)^2 = 90810$
Find the mean and standard deviation of the weights of the fish.

Let y = x - 400.
Write down $\sum y =$ and $\sum y^2 =$
Find the mean of y and add 400 to find the mean of x.

Find the variance and hence the standard deviation of y. This is the same as the standard deviation of x.

Box and whisker plots or box plots:
This diagrammatic representation of data shows the location and spread of the data.
Scale:

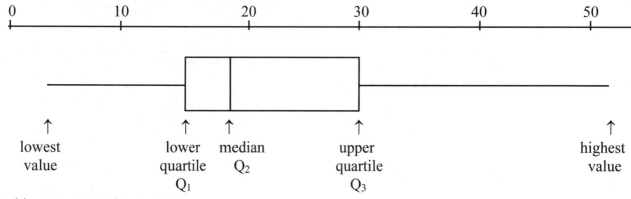

From this you can work out:
  • the median, the upper and lower quartiles
  • The spread of the middle 50% (the interquartile range)
  • the extreme values and the range
  • the 'shape' of the distribution

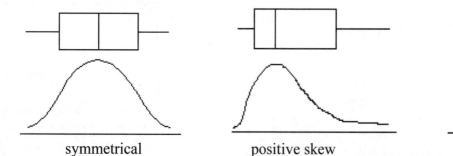

Note: the median divides the area of the histogram into two equal halves.

Example: Twenty people were asked to estimate the length of a line to the nearest cm. Their replies were as follows:

9, 13, 12, 7, 11, 12, 11, 11, 13, 10, 13, 8, 12, 12, 10, 12, 13, 15, 6, 12.

Draw a box plot and comment on the shape of the distribution.

Complete:

put the data in order.

Median Q_2 = Q_1 = Q_3 =

Find the median and quartiles (write them down!)

Draw the box plot.

```
 ┬   ┬   ┬   ┬   ┬   ┬   ┬   ┬   ┬   ┬   ┬
 6   7   8   9   10  11  12  13  14  15  16
```

Comment.

Mixed questions:

1. The following are the numbers of students in the classes in a college.

   15, 10, 9, 20, 23, 23, 29, 38, 32, 26, 16, 18, 20, 28, 29, 31, 14, 7, 5, 12, 16, 24, 15, 17, 16, 22, 27, 23, 24, 25, 26, 14.

   Work out the mean and standard deviation of class size.

   Draw a stem and leaf diagram.
   Find the median and quartiles.
   Draw a box-and-whisker plot for the data.

2. The estimated speeds of a sample of 30 vehicles travelling along a stretch of road are shown below.

```
1 | 4
2 | 4 6 6 8 8
3 | 0 2 4 4 6 8 8 8
4 | 0 0 2 2 2 4 8
5 | 0 2 6 6 8
6 | 4
7 | 0 4            key  6 | 4 means 64 mph
8 | 2
```

Describe shape of the distribution.
Find the median and quartiles and draw a box-and-whisker plot.
Work out the mean and standard deviation.

3. The readings, x from an experiment are coded using $y = x - 20$. If the mean and standard deviation of y are 23 and 1.2 respectively Write down the mean and standard deviation of x.

4. The lengths, x cm, of a sample of 20 components from a production line are summarised by the equations
$$\sum(x-15) = 4 \text{ and } \sum(x-15)^2 = 1.448$$
Find the mean and standard deviation of the sample lengths of components.

5. A stem-and-leaf diagram of some data is shown below.

```
10 | 0 1
15 | 1 2 2 3 3 3
20 | 0 2 3 4 4
25 | 0 1 4
30 | 3
35 | 2 3
40 | 0            key  25 | 1 represents 26
```

(i) Describe the shape of the distribution.
(ii) Find the values of
    (a) the median
    (b) the interquartile range
    (c) the mode

FREQUENCY TABLES

The marks obtained by 50 students in a test are summarised below

mark	0	1	2	3	4	5	6	7	8	9	10
no. of students	1	2	2	3	6	9	12	7	5	2	1

The mode:
this is the value that occurs most often. The mode is 6 marks. (Careful: A common mistake is to put 12 for the mode.)

The median:
this is the middle value once the data have been arranged in order. If there are two numbers in the middle add them up and divide by two.

Here the scores are already in order.
Two halves of 25 so the median is given by the 25th and 26th students. (or ½ (n + 1)[th] student)
Count up to see where the 25th and 26th students are.
Here they both have a score of 6 so
The median is 6 marks.

The mean:

add up all the values and divide by the number of values.

$$\bar{x} = \frac{\sum fx}{\sum f}$$

The variance and standard deviation:

$$\text{Variance} = \frac{\sum f(x-\bar{x})^2}{\sum f} \qquad \text{or} \quad \text{variance} = \frac{\sum fx^2}{\sum f} - \bar{x}^2$$

The second version is usually easier to set out and use. Sometimes exam questions give $\sum f$, $\sum fx$ and $\sum fx^2$ - so you need to be able to use this form.

Standard Deviation is the square root of the variance

LEARN THESE - **not** in formula book

Complete:

mark, x	numbers of students, f	fx	x^2	fx^2
0	1	$1 \times 0 = 0$	$0^2 = 0$	$1 \times 0 = 0$
1	2	$2 \times 1 = 2$	$1^2 = 1$	$2 \times 1 = 2$
2	2	$2 \times 2 = 4$	$2^2 = 4$	$2 \times 4 = 8$
3	3			
4	6	$6 \times 4 =$		
5	9		$5^2 =$	
6	12			$12 \times 36 =$
7	7			
8	5			
9	2			
10	1			
	$\sum f =$	$\sum fx =$		$\sum fx^2 =$

Mean, $\bar{x} = \dfrac{\sum fx}{\sum f} = \underline{\quad} =$

Variance $= \dfrac{\sum fx^2}{\sum f} - \bar{x}^2 = \underline{\quad\quad} - \quad =$

Standard deviation, sd $= \sqrt{\underline{\quad\quad}} =$

1. For the following frequency table find the mean and standard deviation of marks

Mark	Frequency			
9	5			
10	9			
11	12			
12	6			
13	2			
Totals				

Ans 10.7, 1.09

2. For a particular set of numbers $\sum f = 29$, $\sum fx = 116$ and $\sum fx^2 = 498$. Find the mean and standard deviation of the set of numbers.

Use the formulae.

   Mean, $\bar{x}$ =

   Variance =

   Standard deviation = $\sqrt{}$ =

Answers 4, 1.08

Enter the following as data items/lists and hence find the mean and standard deviation either direct from your calculator or by obtaining Σx, Σy etc. and using the formula.

3. Find the mean and standard deviation for each of the following frequency tables

a)

Score	5	6	7	8	9	10	11	12
Frequency	3	5	8	15	11	6	4	1

b)

Goals	0	1	2	3	4
Frequency	10	21	12	5	1

c)

Points	0	1	2	3	4	5	6	7	8
Frequency	8	5	2	4	7	6	5	1	2

Working with grouped data:

Histograms:

When you draw a histogram:

- First establish the boundaries for each interval
  e.g. for height of plants that have been measured to the nearest cm, in the interval 20 - 24, the lower boundary is 19.5 and the upper boundary is 24.5   (be careful with age)
- Find each interval width
  width = upper boundary - lower boundary

  The group 20 - 24 years has boundaries at 20 and 24.9999......because you are 19 right up to the day you become 20 etc.

- For a histogram

  The area represents the frequency   The area is proportional to frequency

  So when the constant of proportionality is 1 (the easiest form to consider)

  frequency = interval width × height of block

  therefore   height of block   = frequency density = $\dfrac{\text{Frequency}}{\text{interval width}}$

Example: The following table shows the heights of a sample of plants. Complete the table and histogram.

Height of plants (cm)	Frequency	Class width	Frequency Density
5-14	10	10	$10 \div 10 = 1$
15-19	12	5	$12 \div 5 = 2.4$
20-24	20		
25-29	18		
30-34	12		
35-39	6		
40-44	4		
45-54	4		

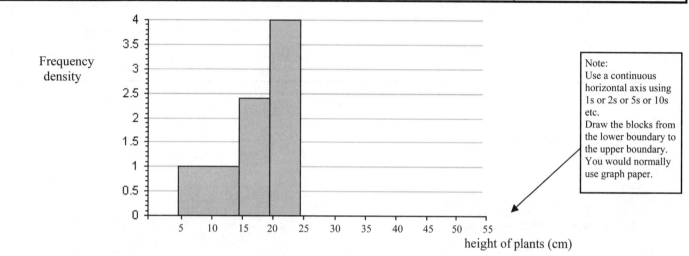

Frequency density

height of plants (cm)

Note:
Use a continuous horizontal axis using 1s or 2s or 5s or 10s etc.
Draw the blocks from the lower boundary to the upper boundary. You would normally use graph paper.

Modal group:

When data values are grouped the modal group is that with the largest frequency density. When all the groups have the same width (as they do in a stem and leaf diagram) the group with the greatest frequency is the modal group.

If two values or two groups occur more frequently than the others, and the stem and leaf diagram or histogram has a "double hump" appearance, the distribution is said to be BI-MODAL, even if one "hump" is taller than the other.

Mean, variance and standard deviation from grouped data:

Here we assume that the members in each group have a mean that is the middle of the group.
We can then use the formulae as for a frequency table taking the midpoint for x.

$$\text{Mean, } \bar{x} = \frac{\sum fx}{\sum f}$$

LEARN THESE - **not** in formula book

$$\text{Variance} = \frac{\sum f(x-\bar{x})^2}{\sum f} \quad \text{or} \quad \text{variance} = \frac{\sum fx^2}{\sum f} - \bar{x}^2$$

The second formula is usually easier to set out and use.

$$\text{Standard Deviation, } \sigma = \sqrt{\frac{\sum f(x-\bar{x})^2}{\sum f}} \quad \text{or} \quad \sigma = \sqrt{\frac{\sum fx^2}{\sum f} - \bar{x}^2}$$

The second formula is usually easier to set out and use.

Be careful when working out the midpoint of a group (e.g. for the above group 5-14 should it be 9.5 or 10?)
To find the midpoint of a group add the upper and lower boundaries and divide by 2.

For the above groups   5 - 14   midpoint $(4.5 + 14.5) \div 2 = 9.5$
                15 - 19   midpoint $(14.5 + 19.5) \div 2 = 17$
                etc.

From the previous table
Complete:

Height of plants (cm)	Frequency f	Midpoint of group, x	fx	x^2	fx^2
5-14	10	9.5	$10 \times 9.5 = 95$	$9.5^2 = 90.25$	$10 \times 90.25 = 902.5$
15-19	12	17	$12 \times 17 =$	$17^2 =$	
20-24	20				
25-29	18				
30-34	12				
35-39	6				
40-44	4				
45-54	4				
	$\sum f =$		$\sum fx =$		$\sum fx^2 =$

Estimates

Mean, $\quad \bar{x} = \dfrac{\sum fx}{\sum f} = \underline{\quad} = $

Variance $= \dfrac{\sum fx^2}{\sum f} - \bar{x}^2 = \underline{\qquad} - \qquad =$

Standard deviation $= \sqrt{\underline{\qquad}} =$

---

1. The following table shows the distances moved in an hour by a random sample of a particular animal. Estimate the mean and standard deviation for this distribution.

Distance(m)	frequency f				
50-99	2				
100-149	5				
150-199	15				
200-249	11				
250-299	6				

Totals

Use the mid-class values

Label columns.

Mean

Variance of sample

Standard deviation

---

2. Estimate the mean and standard deviation for this distribution.

Length (cm)	10 - 19	20 - 29	30 - 39	40 - 49	50 - 59
Frequency	6	12	40	17	5

Write down the mid class values.
Then try using your calculator for this one.

3. Phil collects data on the heights of 40 students (all those taking Maths) and records them as shown
   Calculate the mean and standard deviation of the height.

height(m)	1.48-1.52	1.53-1.57	1.58-1.62	1.63-1.67	1.68-1.72	1.73-1.77	1.78-1.82	1.83-1.87	1.88-1.92
frequency	2	4	5	8	10	7	3	0	1

Cumulative frequency:

You have met this at GCSE so an example should remind you what to do.

Example: The table shows the distribution of times taken by 100 people to complete a task.

Time(sec)	Frequency	Cumulative frequency
20-29	3	
30-39	14	
40-49	25	
50-59	30	
60-69	18	
70-79	9	
80-89	1	

Here you must complete the cumulative frequency column.

Use graph paper for cumulative frequency in exams.

Use a continuous horizontal axis going up in 1s or 2s or 5s or 10s (It will be easier to read off values when finding the median etc)

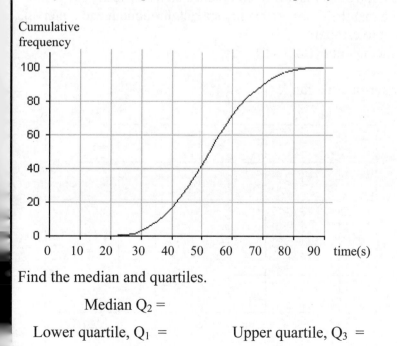

Establish the boundaries for each interval

Remember to plot top of the group against cumulative frequency.
i.e. 29.5 and 3
39.5 and 17
49.5 and 42
etc.

Find the median and quartiles.

      Median Q_2 =

Lower quartile, Q_1 =   Upper quartile, Q_3 =

Inter quartile range =

Draw the lines on the graph. Be as accurate as possible and read off the values as accurately as you can. This will be easier to do on graph paper.

Upper quartile - lower quartile

Mixed questions:

1.

Length	Frequency		
$0 \leq x < 20$	10		
$20 \leq x < 25$	12		
$25 \leq x < 30$	18		
$30 \leq x < 40$	10		

The table shows the heights of 50 seedlings.
Draw a histogram to illustrate the data.
(hint: frequency density up the vertical axis)

2. Find the mean and standard deviation for this frequency table

SCORE	FREQUENCY
10	5
11	8
12	12
13	6
14	1

3. This frequency distribution shows the times taken by 30 students to complete a statistics test. Times are given to the nearest minute and you can assume that the times are evenly spread throughout each interval. Draw the cumulative frequency curve and use it to estimate

Time (min)	Frequency
5 - 9	2
10 - 14	3
15 - 19	16
20 - 24	8
25 - 34	1

(i) the median time (to 3 s.f.)

(ii) the inter-quartile range (to 3 s.f.)

4. A frequency table where the variable x is coded is summarised by the equations

$$\sum f = 40 \ , \ \sum f(x - 30) = 320 \quad \text{and} \quad \sum f(x - 30)^2 = 2920$$

Find the mean and standard deviation of the variable x.

5. The table shows the values of orders (to the nearest £) taken by a make-up and toiletries representative selling house-to-house over a month. No order is over £40.

Value of order	no. of orders				
less than £3	2				
£3 to less than £6	5				
£6 to less than £9	12				
£9 to less than £12	8				
£12 to less than £15	9				
£15 to less than £20	1				
£20 to less than £40	3				

(i) Estimate the mean and standard deviation for these data.

(ii) Draw the cumulative frequency curve and use it to estimate the median and the inter quartile range.

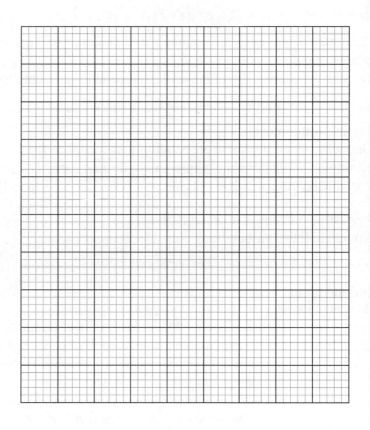

PROBABILITY

Assuming all outcomes are equally likely

> Probability of an event happening   = $\underline{\text{The number of possible outcomes that include the event}}$
> The total number of possible outcomes

If you cannot work out the probability from knowing 'equally likely outcomes' then you need to use relative frequency as an estimate of the probability.

> Estimation of probability   = $\underline{\text{The number of outcomes that include the event}}$
> The total number of trials

Notation: Probability of A happening is written P(A)
          Number of ways event A has occurred is written   n(A)
          A′ is the event 'not A' i.e. the event A does not happen

If an event will never occur, the probability of that event happening is 0
If an event will definitely occur, the probability of that event happening is 1
All other probabilities lie between 0 and 1. Write them as a fraction or a decimal (or a percentage).

A fair dice is thrown
The probability of getting a six is written P(six) or P(6)   and so $P(6) = \frac{1}{6}$

The probability of an event NOT happening
        P(will not happen) = 1 - P(will happen)

Example
A fair dice is thrown
  $P(6) = \frac{1}{6}$ $P(\text{not a }6) = 1 - \frac{1}{6} = \frac{5}{6}$

The addition law:
If two events are mutually exclusive, that is they both cannot happen at the same time,

then   > P(A or B) = P(A) + P(B)

Example: There are 5 red counters, 4 blue counters, 9 green counters and 2 white counters in a bag. One is taken at random.
What is the probability of picking a red counter or a white counter?

        $P(\text{Red or White}) = P(\text{Red}) + P(\text{White}) = \frac{5}{20} + \frac{2}{20} = \frac{7}{20}$

Listing outcomes:
One way of solving some probability questions is to list equally likely outcomes.
Example A 10p coin and a 2p coin are thrown together
Possible outcomes   HH , HT , TH , TT   (Note: HT is different from TH i.e. a head on the 10p and a tail on
                                the 2p is different from a tail on the 10p and a head on the 2p)

4 possible outcomes, all equally likely.
Complete these probabilities.

  P(2 heads) = ———   P(at least one head) = ———

> Note: at least one head is one head or more than one head. Can be found by 1 - P(no heads)

Independent events:
(Multiplication rule)
Here the occurrence of one event, A has no effect on the other, B.
e.g. Drawing a king then a queen from a pack of cards if the first one drawn is replaced. $\frac{4}{52} \times \frac{4}{52}$

> Independent events P(A and B) = P(A and B) = P(A) × P(B)

If you are asked to show that events are independent you must work out the probabilities: P(A) , P(B) and
P(A ∩ B) and then work out P(A) × P(B) to see if is the same as P(A ∩ B). If it is you can then say
"therefore A and B are independent"

Some questions for you to try.

1. A card is picked at random from a pack of 52 playing cards. Find
  a) P(black) =
 	
  b) P(club) =
 	
  c) P(king) =
 	
  d) P(king or ace) =
	Probability of picking a black card.
	26 black cards out of 52 cards and simplify the fraction.
	Probability of picking a club.
	
	Probability of picking a king.
	
	Probability of picking a king or an ace. OR so use addition rule.

2. A coin is thrown and a four sided spinner labelled 1, 2, 3 and 4 is spun. Find
  a) P(head and 2)
 	
  b) P(head and even)
	Independent events .
	Probability of throwing a head and a two.
	AND, so use multiplication rule.
	
	Probability of throwing a head and an even number.

3. The probability that James is late arriving at the bus stop is $\frac{1}{4}$ and the probability that the bus is late arriving at the bus stop is $\frac{1}{3}$. Find a) the probability that James is not late arriving at the bus stop. b) the probability that James and the bus are both late arriving at the bus stop.	 *1 - P(late)* *AND so use the multiplication rule*

4. Three coins are thrown. List all the possible outcomes.
 	
  Find a) P(3 tails)
 	
      b) P(At least one tail)
 	
      c) P(Exactly 2 heads)
	You should get 8
	
	a) How many outcomes give this result? Write as a fraction out of the total number of possible outcomes.
	
	b) Can be found by 1 - P(no tails). OR by counting outcomes as before.
	
	c) How many outcomes give this result? Write as a fraction out of the total number of possible outcomes.

Possibility diagrams (sample space diagrams) for two events:

A diagram may help when solving problems where there are two events to consider.

Example: Two dice are thrown and the numbers showing are multiplied to give a score.

This diagram shows the possible outcomes.

2nd dice

1st dice	×	1	2	3	4	5	6
	1	1	2	3	4	5	6
	2	2	4	6	8	10	12
	3	3	6	9	12	15	18
	4	4	8	12	16	20	24
	5	5	10	15	20	25	30
	6	6	12	18	24	30	36

5. a) What is the total number of possible outcomes?

b) Find P(score 18) =

c) Find P(score 4) =

d) Find P(score is odd) =

e) Find P(score is even) =

6. A coin and a dice are thrown. Find Complete this table to show the possible outcomes.

dice

coin		1	2	3			
	H	H1	H2				
	T	T1					

Only the shaded part gives you the outcomes.

Independent events - could be worked out using the multiplication law.

Find a) P(Head and 6) =

     b) P(Tail and odd) =

Dependent events:
the occurrence of one event effects the other.
e.g. Drawing a king then a queen from a pack of cards if the first one drawn is <u>not</u> replaced. $\frac{4}{52} \times \frac{4}{51}$

> Dependent events   P(A and B) = P(A and B) = P(A) × P(B | A)

the probability of B given A has occurred

Tree diagrams:

We may use tree diagrams to help us to understand a probability question.

Example: There are 3 red discs and 5 blue discs in a bag. A disc is chosen without looking, its colour noted and then a second disc is chosen.
Find the probability that the discs are (i) both red   (ii) different colours.

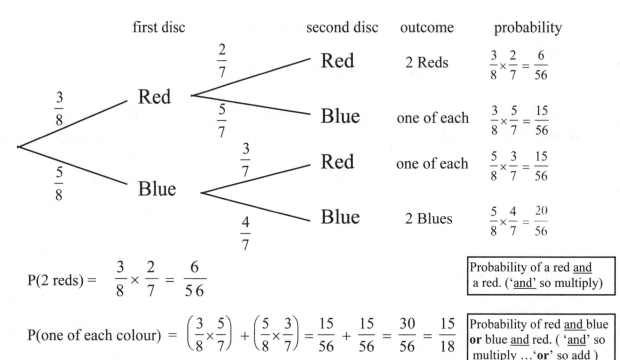

	first disc	second disc	outcome	probability
		$\frac{2}{7}$ Red	2 Reds	$\frac{3}{8} \times \frac{2}{7} = \frac{6}{56}$
$\frac{3}{8}$	Red	$\frac{5}{7}$ Blue	one of each	$\frac{3}{8} \times \frac{5}{7} = \frac{15}{56}$
		$\frac{3}{7}$ Red	one of each	$\frac{5}{8} \times \frac{3}{7} = \frac{15}{56}$
$\frac{5}{8}$	Blue	$\frac{4}{7}$ Blue	2 Blues	$\frac{5}{8} \times \frac{4}{7} = \frac{20}{56}$

$$\text{P(2 reds)} = \frac{3}{8} \times \frac{2}{7} = \frac{6}{56}$$

Probability of a red <u>and</u> a red. ('<u>and</u>' so multiply)

$$\text{P(one of each colour)} = \left(\frac{3}{8} \times \frac{5}{7}\right) + \left(\frac{5}{8} \times \frac{3}{7}\right) = \frac{15}{56} + \frac{15}{56} = \frac{30}{56} = \frac{15}{18}$$

Probability of red <u>and</u> blue or blue <u>and</u> red. ('<u>and</u>' so multiply …'**or**' so add)

We can also understand **conditional probability** from looking at a tree diagram.
         P(Red ∩ Blue) =   P(Red) × P(Blue given Red has occurred)

$$\text{P(R} \cap \text{B)} =   \text{P(R) × P(B | R)}$$

Dependent events

or rearranging $\text{P(B | R)} = \dfrac{\text{P(R and B)}}{\text{P (R)}}$ or $\dfrac{\text{P(B and R)}}{\text{P (R)}}$

For P(B | R) we say "the probability of B given R has occurred".

Here we are looking at two trials but the result is also true for a single trial
e.g. a card is picked at random from a set of playing cards. Given that the card is red find the probability that

it is a heart. $\text{P(heart | red)} = \dfrac{P(heart \ and \ red)}{P(red)} = \dfrac{\frac{13}{52}}{\frac{26}{52}} = \frac{13}{26} = \frac{1}{2}$

Which makes sense. If you know you have a red card of which there are 26 in a pack and 13 of these are hearts then P(heart | red) = $\frac{13}{26}$ = $\frac{1}{2}$

In general:

$$P (A | B) = \frac{P(A \ and \ B)}{P(B)}$$

1. A student either walks to college or he catches a bus. The probability that he walks is 0.6. If he walks, the probability that he is late is 0.1. If he catches the bus, the probability that he is late is 0.2 Complete the tree diagram to show this information.

```
                                            LATE
                    WALK  <

        <

                    BUS   <
```

a) What is the probability that the student walks and is <u>not</u> late?

b) What is the probability that the student is late?

2. Two people A and B play three games of darts. The probabilty that A wins the first game is $\frac{2}{5}$. In the next two games the probability that A or B wins is $\frac{4}{5}$ if they win the previous game. There are no drawn games.   (i) Draw a tree diagram to represent this information.
(ii) Find the probability that B wins all three games.
(iii) Find the probability that B wins two games out of the three.

For two events A and B

```
                                          P(B|A)      B          A and B  <--- P(A and B)
                        P(A)      A  <
                                          1 - P(B|A)  not B      A               These added give P(A)
        <
                                          P(B|A')     B          B               These added give P(B)
                        1 - P(A)  not A <
                                          1 - P(B|A') not B      neither  <--- P(A' and B')
```
                                                                 outcome

3. If P(A) = 0.6, P(B|A) = 0.7 and P(B'|A') = 0.2, find
  (i) P(A and B) (ii) P(B) (iii) P(A|B)

```
                            B
              A    <
                            not B
        <
                            B
            not A  <
                            not B
```

(i) P(A and B)

(ii) P(B)

(iii) P(A|B)

First draw a tree diagram with the probabilities on the branches. You should be able to complete them all.
Multiply along the branches to obtain P(A and B), P(A and B'), P(A' and B), P(A' and B').
(i)From the tree.
(ii)
Add the two outcomes that give B.
(iii)
Use $P(A|B) = \frac{P(B\,and\,A)}{P(B)} = \frac{P(A\,and\,B)}{P(B)}$
i.e. given the first and third probabilities from the tree diagram, what is the probability it is the first one.

Mixed questions

1. Find the probability of obtaining at least one six in a throw of 3 dice.	*At least one six is the opposite of no sixes.* *P(at least 1 six) = 1 - P(no sixes)* *So need to find P(no six and no six and no six) i.e. the multiplication rule.*
2. In a game for 2 players a turn consists of throwing a die once or twice. If a player throws less than 6 on the first throw, the score is the score on the die. If a player throws a 6 on the first throw, she throws again and her score is the total score of the two throws. Find the probabilities of (i) scoring more than 9 in a turn (ii) scoring a total of more than 20 in two successive turns (iii) obtaining equal scores in two successive turns.	*List the pairs that give a score of more than 9* *For (ii) again list the possibilities and write down the probability of getting the scores. Work out the probability.* *A table of probabilities of each score will help for (iii)*

3. A student walks or cycles to college. The probability that she cycles is 0.3. If she walks to college the probability that she is late is 0.35 and if she cycles the probability that she is late is 0.15.
(a) Find the probability that she is late on any particular day.
(b) Given that she is late one day find the probability that she walked.
(c) Given that she is not late one day find the probability that she walked.
	Draw a tree diagram.
	
	a) find the outcomes that give her as late and add them.
	
	b) Use the tree diagram or the formula for P (A | B) looking for
	  • *the outcome that gives walk and late*
	  • *The outcomes that give late*
	
	c) similar to b.

ARRANGEMENTS AND SELECTIONS

An ARRANGEMENT or a PERMUTATION of a given number of objects is a group of objects chosen from those given where the order of the objects is taken into consideration.

Consider the letters X Y and Z Permutations of these letters are XYZ, XZY, YXZ, YZX, ZXY and ZYX 6 in total Permutations of 2 letters from X Y and Z are XY, YX, XZ, ZX, YZ and ZY 6 in total	*We want to count the number of PATTERNS of the letters*

A SELECTION or a COMBINATION of a given number of objects is a group of objects chosen from those given where the order of the objects is not taken into consideration.

Consider the letters X Y and Z again There is only 1 combination of these letters containing all three letters: it is XYZ There are 3 combinations of 2 letters chosen from X Y and Z They are XY, XZ and YZ	*Look for a COLLECTION of letters.* *This is the same as ZXY or any other way of writing the three letters. Here order doesn't matter.*

AN IMPORTANT PRINCIPLE TO REMEMBER
If one operation can be done in A ways and a second operation can be done in B ways then the number of different ways in which both operations can be done is A×B
This principle can be extended to three or more operations as you can see in the following examples

Example: If we were to invent a new language where every word consisted of one consonant followed by one vowel, how many words would this language contain?
 	
Assuming we have 21 consonants and 5 vowels we can select 1 consonant for the first letter (a choice from 21 possibilities) and 1 vowel for the second letter (a choice from 5 possibilities), so the number of words is
     $21 \times 5 = 105$ words.
 	
If we now extend the language by adding in two letter words with a vowel as the first letter and a consonant as the second letter, the number of new words will be
     $5 \times 21 = 105$
 	
We could now add in two consonant words: the number of new words here, assuming that we do not allow double letters is
     $21 \times 20 = 420$
In a similar way two vowel words with no repeats of letters will mean
     $5 \times 4 = 20$ new words.
 	
So altogether we now have a language of 650 words.
	We have 21 choices for the first letter, but having used one consonant up for the first letter and not being allowed repeats means only 20 choices for the second letter

Complete: There are 4 seats in a taxi. In how many ways can 3 people seat themselves? There are 4 possibilities for the first seat - it could be the free one or have any of the 3 people sitting in it. Then there are 3 possibilities for the second seat and so on. ☐ × ☐ × ☐ × ☐ Put the numbers in the boxes So the number of seating arrangements (each with 3 people and one empty seat) is _____	*Consider the 4 seats as boxes that you wish to fill. How many ways can you fill each box? Multiply your answers together.*
Complete: How many different ways are there of predicting the results of 5 football matches? Assuming that the result of each match can be WIN, LOSE or DRAW, there are three possible outcomes for <u>each</u> match. ☐ × ☐ × ☐ × ☐ × ☐ The total number of predictions is _____	*Put the number of possibilities for each match in each box*

Arrangements of unlike quantities:

The number of ways of arranging n unlike objects is n!

If we only want to arrange r of the n unlike objects, the number of ways is $\dfrac{n!}{(n-r)!}$

In order to illustrate this consider the following examples.

---

1. In how many ways can 8 different books be arranged on a bookshelf, leaving no gaps?

Complete:

Imagine the 8 places for the books to be boxes.

You have 8 choices for the first box, 7 for the next, …….

□×□×□×□×□×□×□×□   Fill the numbers in the boxes.

The 8 books can be arranged in_____ways, which is 8!

---

2. If the bookshelf can only hold 5 books, how many arrangements are there?

□×□×□×□×□

There are 8 choices for the first space, 7 for the next, …

The number of arrangements is _____ or $\dfrac{8!}{3!}$

In general if we want the number of ways of arranging r objects from a set of n objects the number is

$$^{n}P_r = \frac{n!}{(n-r)!}$$

The P stands for Permutation

Fill in the boxes

$\dfrac{8!}{3!} = \dfrac{8\times7\times6\times5\times4\times3\times2\times1}{3\times2\times1}$

---

3. Find the number of ways of

   (a) arranging 7 ornaments on a mantlepiece

Use boxes if it helps. 7 choices for the first, 6 for the second etc. You should be calculating $^{7}P_7$

 (b) arranging 4 of the ornaments in a line on a small shelf

7 choices for the first place, 6 for the second, ... You should be calculating $^{7}P_4$

---

4. In how many different ways can 8 people sit around a table?

There are no ends to a table - so we need to use one person as a marker and sit the others relative to her. Say we sit our first person at the table. We can now assume we have seven places left to fill, working clockwise (or anti clockwise) from her.

Arrangements = _____ = _____

Treat the 7 remaining places as 7 boxes

---

5. Find the number of 3 digit numbers that can be formed using the digits 2,3,4,5

    (a) using each digit only once

    (b) if each digit can be used more than once

    (c) if the numbers must be between 200 and 400 and digits can be used more than once

Arrangement: 3 boxes, 4 numbers

b) Each number can be used in each box

c) Only two digits can be used in the first box.

Combinations:

If we are not interested in the order in which objects are chosen but simply which collection or SELECTION of objects is chosen we need to cancel out the different patterns of the same group of objects and only count it once.

Example: If a committee of 2 is to be chosen from 6 people, A, B, C, D, E, & F how many committees are possible?

6×5 or $\dfrac{6!}{4!}$ gives the number of arrangements of people but A & B and B & A should not be counted as 2 different committees and nor should C & E and E & C be counted twice. We have twice as many committees as we want! So the number of DIFFERENT committees is $\dfrac{6!}{4!2!}$

In general, if we are selecting r objects from a group of n objects, the different number of selections we can make is

$$\frac{n!}{(n-r)!\,r!} = {}^nC_r = \binom{n}{r}$$ where the C stands for COMBINATION

---

6. A mixed volleyball team is to be picked from 7 boys and 5 girls. The rules of the game say that at least 3 girls must be on court at any time. The coach chooses 3 girls and 3 boys: How many different teams can he pick?

Choose 3 girls from 5 means ${}^5C_3 =$ _____

Choose 3 boys from 7 means ${}^7C_3 =$ _____

Each choice of 3 girls could be teamed with any choice of 3 boys, so the total number of possible teams is
   ${}^5C_3 \times {}^7C_3 =$ _____

We are using the A×B principle here mentioned earlier

---

7. There are 8 foreign coins and 6 British coins in a purse. Each coin has a different value. If a handful of these coins includes 4 foreign and 5 British coins, how many different handfuls could there be?

Number of handfuls =

Calculate the combinations of foreign coins first, then multiply by the number of British combinations.

If you are selecting or choosing a number of objects from a set of objects that have 2 or more identical object then look at each of the cases when none are included, one is included 2 are included, etc and add them.
e.g. How many ways can 4 letters be chosen from the word FOOLISH.
   No 0s ${}^5C_4 = 5$ One 0 ${}^5C_3 = 10$ Two 0s ${}^5C_2 = 10$ Total choices = 25

Mixed questions

1. A committee is to be formed of 4 men and 5 women from 7 men and 7 women. How many different committees are possible?

Use ${}^nC_r$

One of the men, Mr A. has to be the chairman. How many different committees are now possible?

Mr. A is already on the committee so just pick the rest of the committee

Mr A. is the chairman, but Mrs B. will not sit on the committee if Mr. C is on it and vice versa. How many committees are now possible?

Consider three scenarios - one with Mrs B. on the committee, one with Mr. C and one without either

2. A netball team of 1 centre, 2 shooters and 4 utility players is to be picked from a squad of 3 centres, 5 shooters and 8 utility players. (a) How many different teams can be chosen?	
The whole squad travel to a tournament. (b) The last 5 on the coach sort out all the kit. On this occasion all the 5 were utility players. In how many ways can that happen?	*Use ^nC_r*
(c) Find the probability that the last 5 onto the coach would be utility players.	*Find the number of different ways the last 5 on the coach can be made up. Then probability is answer to (b) over this number.*
3. A mixed team of 6 volleyball players is to be chosen from 5 men and 6 women. At least 3 women must be in any team. How many different teams could be chosen?	*Consider in turn the number of teams containing 3, 4, 5 and 6 women and add up to find the total.*
4. Three girls and two boys sit in a row. (a) How many different seating arrangements are there?	$n!$
(b) What is the probability that the boys do not sit next to each other if the children are seated in random order?	*Find the number of ways that the boys do sit together (treat BB as one person but remember B_1B_2 is different from B_2B_1) then subtract from answer from (a). Then find probability.*
5. A hockey team of 11 players is chosen at random from a squad of 20. Find the probability that the only goalkeeper in the squad is picked.	*$^{20}C_{11}$ is number of possible teams.* *$^{19}C_{10}$ is the number of teams containing the goalkeeper.*
6. The digits 2, 3, 4 and 5 are used without repetition to produce 4 digit numbers. How many numbers can be produced?	$n!$
If one of these numbers is chosen at random, what is the probability that it is even and greater than 4000?	*Find out how many numbers fit the description. The thousand digit must be 4 or 5.* *If the thousand digit is 4, the unit digit must be 2. If it is 5 the unit digit must be 2 or 4. Use boxes to look at all possibilities.*

DISCRETE RANDOM VARIABLES

Discrete - can only take particular values.
Random - cannot determine the outcome for any trial.
Variable - can take different numerical values.

Discrete random variables:
If a discrete random variable X can take the values $x_1, x_2, x_3, \ldots\ldots, x_n$ with probabilities $p_1, p_2, p_3, \ldots, p_n$ respectively the **probability distribution** is written

x	x_1	x_2	x_3	....	x_n
$P(X = x)$	p_1	p_2	p_3		p_n

These are the values that the random variable can be

These are the corresponding probabilities

The probability that the random variable equals x

and $$\sum_{i=1}^{i=n} p_i = 1$$

i.e. the probabilities add to give 1

mean or expectation $$\mu = E(X) = \sum_{i=1}^{i=n} x_i\, p_i$$

i.e. multiply the values by their probabilities and add them (to give the mean or expectation)

variance, $$Var(X) = E(X^2) - [\,E(X)\,]^2 = \sum_{i=1}^{i=n} x_i^2\, p_i - [E(X)]^2$$

i.e. square the values and multiply the answers by their probabilities. Add them up and subtract the mean squared.

The standard deviation is the square root of the variance

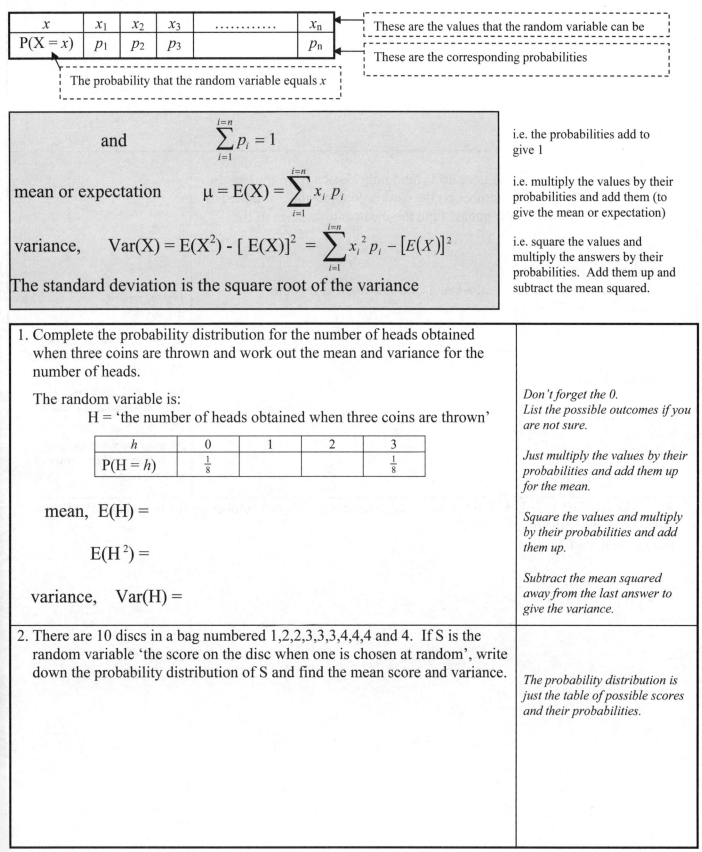

1. Complete the probability distribution for the number of heads obtained when three coins are thrown and work out the mean and variance for the number of heads.

The random variable is:
    H = 'the number of heads obtained when three coins are thrown'

h	0	1	2	3
$P(H = h)$	$\frac{1}{8}$			$\frac{1}{8}$

mean, $E(H) =$

$E(H^2) =$

variance, $Var(H) =$

Don't forget the 0.
List the possible outcomes if you are not sure.

Just multiply the values by their probabilities and add them up for the mean.

Square the values and multiply by their probabilities and add them up.

Subtract the mean squared away from the last answer to give the variance.

2. There are 10 discs in a bag numbered 1,2,2,3,3,3,4,4,4 and 4. If S is the random variable 'the score on the disc when one is chosen at random', write down the probability distribution of S and find the mean score and variance.

The probability distribution is just the table of possible scores and their probabilities.

3. A random variable X has probability function f(x) given by

$$f(x) = \frac{3x+1}{50} \quad ; \quad x = 1, 2, 3, 4, 5$$

Write down the probability distribution of S and find the mean score and variance.

4. Complete:

In a game, at a particular point, a card is randomly chosen from four cards labelled 0, 1, 2 and 3. The number on the card is doubled and 3 is added to give a score to be used in the game. Find the mean and variance of the score.

The random variable is:

S = 'the score obtained when a card is chosen at random'

s	3	5	7	9
P(S = s)				

mean, E(S) =

E(S^2) =

variance,   Var(S) =

List the possible outcomes if you are not sure.

Just multiply the values by their probabilities and add them up for the mean.

Square the values and multiply by their probabilities and add them up.

Subtract the mean squared away from the last answer to give the variance.

5. A fair die labelled 1, 3, 3, 5, 6, 6. If the random variable, X, is the number on the die when rolled, find
   a) the probability distribution for X
   b) E(X) and Var(X)

BINOMIAL DISTRIBUTION

Consider the number of sixes obtained when a fair die is thrown five times.
Note:
* We are interested in only the two outcomes: throw a six (Success) or not throw a six (Failure)
* The probability of obtaining a six is not affected by previous throws (the trials are independent)
* There are a set number of throws (trials) i.e. five

If   S = obtain a six from a throw   and   F = do <u>not</u> obtain a six from a throw

P(no sixes from 5 throws)   i.e.   F F F F F   is given by $\dfrac{5}{6} \times \dfrac{5}{6} \times \dfrac{5}{6} \times \dfrac{5}{6} \times \dfrac{5}{6} = \left(\dfrac{5}{6}\right)^5$

P(one six from 5 throws) i.e. S F F F F   is given by $\dfrac{1}{6} \times \dfrac{5}{6} \times \dfrac{5}{6} \times \dfrac{5}{6} \times \dfrac{5}{6} = \left(\dfrac{1}{6}\right)^1 \left(\dfrac{5}{6}\right)^4$

or F S F F F   is given by $\dfrac{5}{6} \times \dfrac{1}{6} \times \dfrac{5}{6} \times \dfrac{5}{6} \times \dfrac{5}{6} = \left(\dfrac{1}{6}\right)^1 \left(\dfrac{5}{6}\right)^4$

or F F S F F   is given by $\dfrac{5}{6} \times \dfrac{5}{6} \times \dfrac{1}{6} \times \dfrac{5}{6} \times \dfrac{5}{6} = \left(\dfrac{1}{6}\right)^1 \left(\dfrac{5}{6}\right)^4$

or F F F S F   is given by $\dfrac{5}{6} \times \dfrac{5}{6} \times \dfrac{5}{6} \times \dfrac{1}{6} \times \dfrac{5}{6} = \left(\dfrac{1}{6}\right)^1 \left(\dfrac{5}{6}\right)^4$

or F F F F S   is given by $\dfrac{5}{6} \times \dfrac{5}{6} \times \dfrac{5}{6} \times \dfrac{5}{6} \times \dfrac{1}{6} = \left(\dfrac{1}{6}\right)^1 \left(\dfrac{5}{6}\right)^4$

> The number of ways of choosing one place for the S from five places is
>
> $^5C_1$ or $\dbinom{5}{1}$
>
> So there are
> $^5C_1 = 5$ lots of
> $\left(\dfrac{1}{6}\right)^1 \left(\dfrac{5}{6}\right)^4$

P(one six) $= {}^5C_1 \left(\dfrac{1}{6}\right)^1 \left(\dfrac{5}{6}\right)^4$ or $\dbinom{5}{1}\left(\dfrac{1}{6}\right)^1 \left(\dfrac{5}{6}\right)^4$

P(two sixes from 5 throws) i.e. S S F F F   is given by $\dfrac{1}{6} \times \dfrac{1}{6} \times \dfrac{5}{6} \times \dfrac{5}{6} \times \dfrac{5}{6} = \left(\dfrac{1}{6}\right)^2 \left(\dfrac{5}{6}\right)^3$

or S F S F F   is given by $\dfrac{1}{6} \times \dfrac{5}{6} \times \dfrac{1}{6} \times \dfrac{5}{6} \times \dfrac{5}{6} = \left(\dfrac{1}{6}\right)^2 \left(\dfrac{5}{6}\right)^3$

or

(List the other arrangements of the letters - you should obtain 10)

> The number of ways of choosing two places for the S from five places is
>
> $^5C_2$ or $\dbinom{5}{2}$
>
> So there are
> $^5C_2 = \dfrac{5.4}{2.1} = 10$
> lots of
> $\left(\dfrac{1}{6}\right)^2 \left(\dfrac{5}{6}\right)^3$

P(two sixes from 5 throws) $= {}^5C_2 \left(\dfrac{1}{6}\right)^2 \left(\dfrac{5}{6}\right)^3$ or $\dbinom{5}{2}\left(\dfrac{1}{6}\right)^2 \left(\dfrac{5}{6}\right)^3$

Notice that although we have found the probabilities for throwing a die 5 times these probabilities could have been for any binomial situation with 5 trials (and is easily extended for more or less trials) where the probability of success is 1/6 (and easily changed for other probabilities)
Complete: P(three sixes from 5 throws)   =

P(four sixes from 5 throws)   =

P(five sixes from 5 throws)   =

IN GENERAL:

Use the binomial distribution when

- There is a set number of trials
- You are only interested in two outcomes SUCCESS and FAILURE
- The probability of Success is the same for each trial
- The trials are INDEPENDENT

If X is binomially distributed where X = "the number of successes"
then

$$X \sim B(n, p)$$

where   n = the number of trials
         p = the probability of success

and   the probability of r successes,

$$P(X = r) = {}^nC_r \, p^r q^{n-r} \quad \text{or} \quad \binom{n}{r} p^r q^{n-r}$$

where $q = 1 - p$

$${}^nC_r = \binom{n}{r} = \frac{n!}{r!(n-r)!}$$

also   expected or mean number of successes $= n \times p$

Variance, $\sigma^2 = n \times p \times q$

---

1. Example: One in five of shirts produced in a factory is rejected. Find the probability that if six shirts are chosen at random

(a) 1 is rejected   (b) 3 are rejected   (c) at least 3 are rejected

X = the number of rejected shirts in a sample of 5   'success' is a shirt rejected

Write this down.

$$X \sim B\left(6, \frac{1}{5}\right)$$

This means X follows a binomial distribution where the number of trials is 6 and the probability of success is 1/5

Write this down.   *n = 6*
                     p = 1/5

(a) $$P(X = 1) = {}^6C_1 \left(\frac{1}{5}\right)^1 \left(\frac{4}{5}\right)^5$$

This means - the probability that the number of rejected shirts equals 1

Show how you get the answer.

$$= 6 \times \frac{1}{5} \times \frac{1024}{3125} = \frac{6144}{15625} = 0.393216$$

Show working.

(b) $$P(X = 3) = {}^6C_3 \left(\frac{1}{5}\right)^3 \left(\frac{4}{5}\right)^3 = \frac{6.5.4}{3.2.1} \times \frac{1}{125} \times \frac{64}{125} = 0.08192$$

(c) $$P(X \geq 3) = 1 - P(X < 3)$$

$$= 1 - [\, P(X = 0) + P(X = 1) + P(X = 2) \,]$$

P(at least 3) means P(3 or more) which is the same as 1 - P(less than 3) [Or can be worked out as P(X=3) + P(X=4) + P(X=5) + P(X=6)]

Complete:

$$P(X = 0) =$$

Do not forget P(X = 0)!

$$P(X = 1) =$$

$$P(X = 2) =$$

Show working.

$$P(X \geq 3) = 1 - [\qquad + \qquad + \qquad]$$

$$=$$

Work out the answer.

d) If 20 shirts are chosen at random calculate values for the mean and variance for the number of shirts rejected.

X = the number of rejected shirts in a sample of 20 $$X \sim B\left(20, \frac{1}{5}\right)$$

Write this down.   n = 20
                    p = 1/5

Mean $= n \times p =$

Variance $= \sigma^2 = n \times p \times q =$

Show how you get the answer.

2. In a multiple choice test there are 10 questions each with 4 possible
   answers. If a candidate guesses the answers at random, find the
   probability that, out of 10, he scores
   a) 0   b) 1   c) less than 3   d) at least 5
   Calculate values for the mean and variance of his score

Complete:

    X =   *In words.*

    X ~   *The distribution.   n = 10   p = ¼*

(a)   P (X =   ) =   *Write out the formula with the*
                                                          numbers you know.
                                                          Work it out. Show your working.

(b)   P (X =   ) =   *Write out the formula with the*
                                                          numbers you know.
                                                          Work it out. Show your working.

(c)   P (X <   ) = P (X =   ) +   *Add up the probabilities less*
                                                          than 3.
                                                          You will have to work out P(X=2)
                                                          the others you worked out in (a)
                                                          and (b).

(d)   P (X ≥   ) = 1 - P (   )   *Easiest to work out the*
                                                          probabilities that X = 0,1,2,3,4 and
                                                          subtract from 1. As you have
                                                          already worked some out!
                                                          (Longer method would be to work
                                                          out the probabilities that X =
                                                          5,6,7,8,9,10 and add them up)

    Mean = n × p =

  Variance = σ^2 = npq =

3. A three sided spinner, numbered 1 to 3, is spun eight times. If the
   numbers are equally likely to turn up, find the probability of obtaining:
       (a) six 2s
       (b) more than five 2s

n =
p =

Write X = ...

Write X ~ .....

a) Write P(X=........

b) Write P(X>........

Cumulative binomial probability tables:

Binomial Probabilities can be found using the tables in your text book or/and your student handbook. The student handbook of formulas and tables is given to you in the exam and can shorten lengthy calculations - so learn how to use them!

Remember: they give *cumulative* probabilities. So using the extract below for a random variable X where $X \sim B(20, 1/6)$ i.e. $n = 20$ and $p = 1/6$

$P(X = 0) = 0.0261$

$P(X \le 1) = P(X = 0) + P(X = 1) = 0.1304$

$P(X \le 2) = P(X = 0) + P(X = 1) + P(X = 2) = 0.3287$

If you wish to find $P(X = 2)$ you must work out $P(X \le 2) - P(X \le 1)$

i.e. $P(X = 2) = P(X \le 2) - P(X \le 1)$

$= 0.3287 - 0.1304$

$= 0.1983$

n	x	....	1/6	0.200	0.250	0.300	1/3	....	2/3	0.700	0.750
20	0	....	0.0261	0.0115	0.0032	0.0008	0.0003	....			
	1	....	0.1304	0.0692	0.0243	0.0076	0.0033	....			
	2	....	0.3287	0.2061	0.0913	0.0355	0.0176	....			
	3	....	0.5665	0.4114	0.2252	0.1071	0.0604	....			
	4		0.7687	0.6296	0.4148	0.2375	0.1515	....	0.0000		
	5		0.8982	0.8042	0.6172	0.4164	0.2972	....	0.0002	0.0000	
	6		0.9629	0.9133	0.7858	0.6080	0.4793	....	0.0009	0.0003	0.0000
	7		0.9887	0.9679	0.8982	0.7723	0.6615	....	0.0037	0.0013	0.0002
	8		0.9972	0.9900	0.9591	0.8867	0.8095	....	0.0130	0.0051	0.0009
	9		0.9994	0.9974	0.9861	0.9520	0.9081	....	0.0376	0.0171	0.0039
	10		0.9999	0.9994	0.9961	0.9829	0.9624	....	0.0919	0.0480	0.0139
	11		1.0000	0.9999	0.9991	0.9949	0.9870	....	0.1905	0.1133	0.0409
	12			1.0000	0.9998	0.9987	0.9963		0.3385	0.2277	0.1018
	13				1.0000	0.9997	0.9991		0.5207	0.3920	0.2142
	14					1.0000	0.9998		0.7028	0.5836	0.3828
	15						1.0000		0.8485	0.7625	0.5852
	16								0.9396	0.8929	0.7748
	17								0.9824	0.9645	0.9087
	18								0.9967	0.9924	0.9757
	19								0.9997	0.9992	0.9968
	20								1.0000	1.0000	1.0000

1. Complete: For $X \sim B(20, 1/6)$

$P(X \le 6) =$ $P(X \le 7) =$ *Straight from the tables.*

$P(X = 7) =$ *Remember you need to subtract*

$P(X = 4) =$

$P(X < 3) =$ *Careful - here it is < not $\le$*
                                                        So $P(X < 3) = P(X \le 2)$

$P(X > 8) =$ *Careful - here it is > not $\le$*
                                                        So $P(X > 8) = 1 - P(X \le 8)$

2. For $Y \sim B(20, 0.7)$

$P(Y \le 10) =$ $P(Y \le 17) =$ *Straight from the tables.*

$P(Y = 12) =$ *Remember you need to subtract*

$P(Y = 18) =$

$P(Y < 16) =$ *Careful - here it is < not $\le$*
                                                        So $P(Y < 16) = P(Y \le 15)$

$P(Y > 16) =$ *Careful - here it is > not $\le$*
                                                        So $P(Y > 16) = 1 - P(Y \le 16)$

$P(Y \ge 14) =$ *Careful - here it is $\ge$ not $\le$*
                                                        So $P(Y \ge 14) = 1 - P(Y \le 13)$

3. A packet of sweets contains red or yellow sweets. In the factory twice as
   many red sweets are mixed with the yellow sweets before a machine
   randomly puts them into packets of twenty sweets.
   (a) Find the probability that a packet contains at least 15 red sweets.
   The packets are then put into bags that hold five packets.
   (b) Find the probability that a bag contains at least 3 packets containing at
   least 15 red sweets?

(a)   X =

         X ~

P(X ≥ 15) =

             =

             =

(b)   Y =

         Y ~

P(Y ≥   ) =

In words - the number of......

The distribution

$= 1 - P(X \leq 14)$

From tables.

The answer.

Careful! This is a different Binomial situation. Success is a packet having at least 15 red sweets. Failure is not . The number of trials (packets) is 5. The probability of success is the answer to part (a)
Use 1 - again.

The probability is not in the tables! You will have to work out some probabilities here!

Mixed questions

1. If X ~ B (8 , 0.4), find (i) P(X ≤ 2)   (ii) P(X = 4)

2. If Z ~ B (6 , 0.225) , find (i) P(Z = 5) (ii) P(Z > 4)

3. If Y ~ B (10 , ¼) , find (i) P(Y ≤ 3) (ii) P(Y = 3)

4. If X ~ B (6 , 3/8) , find (i) P(X < 2) (ii) P(X ≤ 2)

5. The probability a darts player hits the bull (when aiming for it) is 0.7.   Assuming independence,
   what is the probability that he gets at least six bulls from nine throws?

6. If X ~ B (n , 0.4) and P (X ≤ 5) = 0.7535 , find n.

7. Three dice are thrown. Write down the probabilities of obtaining 0 , 1 , 2 and 3 ones.

8. Six coins are thrown into the air. Assuming the coins are unbiased what is the probability of obtaining four or more heads?

9. Five fair dice are thrown in a game. What is the probability of obtaining at least three sixes?

For the next *three* questions work out the answers by using the formula for working out the probabilities *and* by using cumulative binomial probability tables (good practice and you can check your answers).

10. The probability a student is late for a lesson is 0.1 . For a period covering 10 lessons, find the probability that he is late
    (i) for exactly 3 lessons
    (ii) for less than 3 lessons

11. A bag contains 4 red balls and 6 blue balls. When a ball is drawn, without looking, its colour is noted and the ball is replaced. If eight balls are drawn, find the probability that
    (i) exactly 4 are red
    (ii) less than three are red
    (iii) more than 6 are red.

12. Four out of five dogs eat LAP. In a Dog Show there are ten champions. Find the probability that
   (i) all ten eat LAP
   (ii) at least 8 eat LAP
   (iii) less than half eat LAP

13. In a factory producing light bulbs, the probability that one is faulty is 0.15 . A batch of 20 light bulbs
   is tested. Find the probability that
   (i) less than 2 are faulty
   (ii) 5 are faulty
   (iii) less than 5 are faulty
   (iv) more than 5 are faulty
   (v) at least 5 are faulty.

14. A calculator is used to generate random digits 0 to 9 inclusive. Each digit is equally likely to turn up.
   (i) What is the probability the first digit generated is greater than 5?
   (ii) If ten digits are generated, find the probability there will be less than four digits greater than 5.

GEOMETRIC DISTRIBUTION

Consider: a fair die is thrown until a six is obtained.

Note:

* We are interested in only the two outcomes: throw a six (Success) or not throw a six (Failure)
* The probability of obtaining a six is not affected by previous throws (the trials are independent)
* The probability of obtaining a six is $\frac{1}{6}$ for each throw
* The die is thrown until a six is obtained

Probability of obtaining a six on the first throw = $\frac{1}{6}$

Probability of obtaining a six on the second throw = P(not 6 on first throw **and** a six on second throw)   = $\frac{5}{6} \times \frac{1}{6}$

Probability of obtaining a six on the third throw = P(not 6 **and** not 6 **and** a six on third throw) = $\frac{5}{6} \times \frac{5}{6} \times \frac{1}{6}$ = $\left(\frac{5}{6}\right)^2 \times \frac{1}{6}$

Probability of obtaining a six on the fourth throw = P(not 6 **and** not 6 **and** not 6 **and** a six) = $\frac{5}{6} \times \frac{5}{6} \times \frac{5}{6} \times \frac{1}{6} = \left(\frac{5}{6}\right)^3 \times \frac{1}{6}$

Probability of obtaining a six on the fifth throw = = P(not 6 **and** not 6 **and** not 6 **and** not 6 **and** six)

$$= \frac{5}{6} \times \frac{5}{6} \times \frac{5}{6} \times \frac{5}{6} \times \frac{1}{6} = \left(\frac{5}{6}\right)^4 \times \frac{1}{6}$$

etc

The geometric distribution:

Use the geometric distribution when

- You are only interested in two outcomes SUCCESS and FAILURE
- The probability of SUCCESS is the same for each trial
- The trials are INDEPENDENT
- The trials continue until a SUCCESS is obtained

If X is geometrically distributed where X = "the number of trials up to and including the first success" then

$$X \sim Geo(p)$$ where   p = the probability of success

and   the probability of x trials,

$$P(X=x) = q^{x-1}p \qquad \text{for } x = 1, 2, 3, ...$$

where $q = 1 - p$

also   expected or mean number of successes, $E(X) = \dfrac{1}{p}$

Other useful results

$$P(X>x) = q^x \qquad \text{(e.g. for } P(X>5) \text{ there have been 5 failures.)}$$
$$P(X \geq x) = q^{x-1}$$
$$P(X \leq x) = 1 - P(X>x) = 1 - q^x$$

where $q = 1 - p$

1. For X ~ Geo(¼)		This means X follows a geometric distribution where the probability of success is ¼.
P(X = 1) = P(X = 2) =		
P(X = 3) = P(X = 4) =		
P(X ≥ 3) =		For P(X ≥ 3) there have been 2 failures.
P(X > 3) =		For P(X > 3) there have been 3 failures.
P(X ≤ 3) =		P(X ≤ 3) = 1 - P(X > 3)
2. For Y ~ Geo(0.7)		This means X follows a geometric distribution where the probability of success is 0.7.
P(Y = 2) = P(Y = 3) =		
P(Y = 2 or 3) = P(Y ≤ 5) =		

3. A drawing pin is thrown until it lands point up. Assuming the probability of the drawing pin landing point up is $\frac{2}{5}$

   a) find the probability that the first time the drawing pin lands point up is on the

    i) third throw   ii) fifth throw.

   b) Find the probability that a drawing pin has not landed point up in six throws

   c) Find the probability that less than five throws are required for the drawing pin to land point up.

      X =

      X ~

  (a) (i)

In words
Write X =' the number of......
The distribution.
Write X ~.....
with p =

a)(i) Write P(X=........

4. While working on a project Nikki has a break. She decides to throw darts at a dart board until she scores a triple 20 with one dart. The probability that she scores a triple 20 with one dart on any particular throw is 0.2.

   a) Find the probability that the first dart to score triple 20 occurs on her

    i) second throw   ii) fifth throw.

   b) Find the probability that no dart scores triple 20 in six throws.

   c) Find the probability that less than three throws are required before she scores a triple 20.

5. A bag contains 4 white counters and 1 blue counter. A counter is selected at random from the bag. If the counter is white it is replaced in the bag and another counter selected. This is repeated until a blue counter is selected. Let X be the number of counters selected up to and including the first blue counter.

  (i) State the distribution of X. (ii) Find P(X = 3) (iii) Find P(X < 4) (iv) Find E(X)

6. A random variable Y has a distribution given by Geo (0.1)

  (i) Find P(Y = 5)   (ii) Find the probability P(3 ≤ Y < 5) (iii) Find E(Y)

CORRELATION AND REGRESSION

Correlation and scatter diagrams:

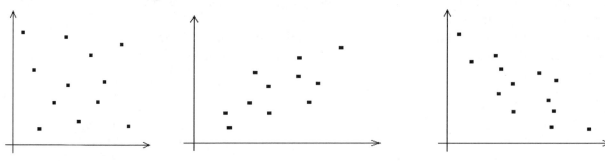

No correlation   Positive correlation   Negative correlation

Product - moment correlation coefficient:

For pairs of values (x_i, y_i)

$$S_{xy} = \sum (x_i - \bar{x})(y_i - \bar{y}) = \sum x_i y_i - \frac{(\sum x_i)(\sum y_i)}{n}$$

$$S_{xx} = \sum (x_i - \bar{x})^2 = \sum x_i^2 - \frac{(\sum x_i)^2}{n} \qquad S_{yy} = \sum (y_i - \bar{y})^2 = \sum y_i^2 - \frac{(\sum y_i)^2}{n}$$

$$r = \frac{S_{xy}}{\sqrt{S_{xx}S_{yy}}} = \frac{\sum (x_i - \bar{x})(y_i - \bar{y})}{\sqrt{\left\{\sum (x_i - \bar{x})^2\right\}\left\{\sum (y_i - \bar{y})^2\right\}}} = \frac{\sum x_i y_i - \frac{(\sum x_i)(\sum y_i)}{n}}{\sqrt{\left(\sum x_i^2 - \frac{(\sum x_i)^2}{n}\right)\left(\sum y_i^2 - \frac{(\sum y_i)^2}{n}\right)}}$$

These are given in your formula book

r lies between -1 and 1. The closer r is to 1 the stronger the positive correlation and the closer r is to -1 the stronger the negative correlation.

You must always be careful with the linear correlation coefficient. Just because two variables indicate good correlation it does not automatically mean they are related - it may be due to another variable or just coincidence. You need to have a reason to suspect that they are connected (or not).

1. Example COMPLETE

x	y	$x - \bar{x}$	$y - \bar{y}$	$(x - \bar{x})(y - \bar{y})$	$(x - \bar{x})^2$	$(y - \bar{y})^2$
11	41					
25	30					
32	31					
46	16					
51	17					
TOTALS						

$\bar{x} =$ $\bar{y} =$

$S_{xx} =$ $S_{yy} =$

$S_{xy} =$

$$r = \frac{S_{xy}}{\sqrt{S_{xx}S_{yy}}} = \underline{\hspace{5cm}} =$$

Comment on the correlation:

Check your answer using a calculator. You should be familiar with how to use your calculator to find r.

2. Example: Find the product moment correlation coefficient for x and y for the following values.

x	1	4	13	16	18	19
y	10	9	11	5	2	1

x	y	x^2	y^2	xy
1	10	1	100	10
4	9	16	81	36
13	11	169	121	143
16	5	256	25	80
18	2	324	4	36
19	1	361	1	19
$\Sigma x=71$	$\Sigma y=38$	$\Sigma x^2=1127$	$\Sigma y^2=332$	$\Sigma xy=324$

Complete:

$$S_{xy} = \sum x_i y_i - \frac{\sum x_i \sum y_i}{n} = \qquad - \underline{\qquad\qquad} =$$

$$S_{xx} = \sum x_i^2 - \frac{\left(\sum x_i\right)^2}{n} = \qquad - \underline{\qquad\qquad} =$$

$$S_{yy} = \sum y_i^2 - \frac{\left(\sum y_i\right)^2}{n} = \qquad - \underline{\qquad\qquad} =$$

$$r = \frac{S_{xy}}{\sqrt{S_{xx}S_{yy}}} = \underline{\qquad\qquad\qquad} =$$

Comment on the correlation:

3. For the following data on the height and weight of ten people find the product moment correlation coefficient.

Weight (Kg) x	Height (cm) y	x^2	y^2	xy
58	156	3364	24336	9048
62	159	3844		
62	163	3844	26569	
64	158	4096		10112
66	166	4356		
72	165		27225	11880
75	170			
76	176			
80	178			
83	176			14608
$\Sigma x =$	$\Sigma y =$	$\Sigma x^2 =$	$\Sigma y^2 =$	$\Sigma xy =$

$$S_{xx} = \sum x_i^2 - \frac{\left(\sum x_i\right)^2}{n} = \qquad - \underline{\qquad} = \qquad\qquad S_{yy} = \sum y_i^2 - \frac{\left(\sum y_i\right)^2}{n} = \qquad - \underline{\qquad} =$$

$$S_{xy} = \sum x_i y_i - \frac{\sum x_i \sum y_i}{n} = \qquad - \underline{\qquad\qquad} =$$

$$r = \frac{S_{xy}}{\sqrt{S_{xx}S_{yy}}} = \underline{\qquad\qquad\qquad} =$$

Comment on the correlation:

Check your answer using a calculator.

4. a) What would a PMCC of 0.99 tell you?

b) What would a PMCC of -0.99 tell you?

c) What would a PMCC of 0.1 tell you?

d) What would a PMCC of -0.1 tell you?

e) What would a PMCC of 0.5 tell you?

f) What would a PMCC of -0.5 tell you?

---

5. Find the product moment correlation coefficient for the following sets of data.

a) $\Sigma x = 135$ $\Sigma y = 65$ $\Sigma x^2 = 3181$ $\Sigma y^2 = 787$ $\Sigma xy = 1561$ $n = 6$

b) $\Sigma (x - \bar{x})^2 = 816$ $\Sigma (y - \bar{y})^2 = 492$ $\Sigma (x - \bar{x})(y - \bar{y}) = 517$

c) $S_{xx} = 2307$ $S_{yy} = 2561$ $S_{xy} = -1894$

---

6. Find the product moment correlation coefficient for the following set of data.

a) $\Sigma x = 110$ $\Sigma y = 422$ $\Sigma x^2 = 1782$ $\Sigma y^2 = 27596$ $\Sigma xy = 4620$ $n = 8$

b) $\Sigma (x - \bar{x})^2 = 641$ $\Sigma (y - \bar{y})^2 = 823$ $\Sigma (x - \bar{x})(y - \bar{y}) = 316$

Using your calculator

Enter the following as data items/lists and hence find r either direct from your calculator or by obtaining Σx, Σy etc. and using the formula.

7. A car rental firm records the age (to the nearest month) of a sample of its cars and the corresponding cost of servicing the cars over the past year.

A (age in months)	12	14	15	18	18	21	22	25
C (service costs in £)	45	100	60	85	100	90	115	120

Calculate the product moment correlation coefficient.

---

8. Find the product moment correlation coefficient for the following set of data.

P	50	60	70	80	90	100	110	120	130	140
Q	5.6	4.8	4.7	4.2	3.9	3.5	3.0	2.6	2.5	2.1

---

9. Find the product moment correlation coefficient for the following set of data.

X	5	6	7	8	9	10
Y	12	20	33	36	42	45

Note: the coding of one or both of the variables has no effect on the value of r.

Spearman's rank correlation coefficient:

$$r_s = 1 - \frac{6\sum d_i^2}{n(n^2 - 1)}$$

where d_i is the difference between ranks

This gives a value to the level of agreement of order between two sets of values which are ranked. r_s lies between -1 (one ranking the complete opposite of the other) and 1(complete agreement between the rankings). Useful when opinions are expressed as in judging a competition or where marks are awarded for qualities such as neatness, taste, accuracy, attractiveness, clarity, etc. and you wish to see if there is any correlation between different judges.

When used for paired scores, measurements, etc. r_s gives a value to how well one variable increases (or decreases) as the other increases, which may not be linear.

---

1. Example COMPLETE

   The following table gives the rankings for six competitors by two judges. Calculate Spearman's rank correlation coefficient and comment on your answer.

Competitor	A	B	C	D	E	F
1st judge	2	1	3	4	6	5
2nd judge	3	2	1	5	4	6
d						
d^2						

   Σ d^2 =

   $$r_s = 1 - \frac{6\sum d_i^2}{n(n^2 - 1)} =$$

---

2. Example COMPLETE

   The table below gives the marks awarded to five divers by two judges in a competition. Calculate Spearman's rank correlation coefficient and comment on your answer.

DIVER	Judge X	Judge Y	X rank	Y rank		
A	8.0	6.0				
B	6.5	7.5				
C	7.0	8.5				
D	9.0	8.0				
E	6.0	6.5				

   Σ d^2 =

   $$r_s = 1 - \frac{6\sum d_i^2}{n(n^2 - 1)} =$$

---

3. The table below gives the scores obtained in a trial examination and the actual examination for S1 in a particular year for ten students. Rank the students in both examinations and calculate Spearman's rank correlation coefficient and comment on your answer.

Trial marks	15	26	34	38	46	52	57	66	71	84
Actual marks	33	28	48	52	51	86	62	95	65	81

Regression line of y on x:
If the y values depend on the x values then x is the independent variable and y is the dependent variable.

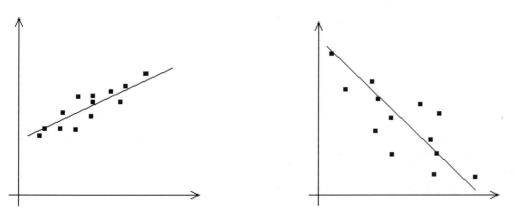

By drawing a scatter diagram you can see whether a straight line is a good model for the relationship between x and y.
The least squares regression line (the line of best fit) of y on x is

$$y = a + bx \quad \text{where} \quad b = \frac{S_{xy}}{S_{xx}} = \frac{\sum(x_i - \bar{x})(y_i - \bar{y})}{\sum(x_i - \bar{x})^2} \quad \text{and} \quad a = \bar{y} - b\bar{x} \quad \text{you may use} \quad y - \bar{y} = b(x - \bar{x})$$

$$S_{xy} = \sum(x_i - \bar{x})(y_i - \bar{y}) = \sum x_i y_i - \frac{(\sum x_i)(\sum y_i)}{n}$$

$$S_{xx} = \sum(x_i - \bar{x})^2 = \sum x_i^2 - \frac{(\sum x_i)^2}{n}$$

Note: this is not given in your formula book.

Note the regression line passes through $(\bar{x}, \bar{y})$

Regression line of x on y:
If the x values depend on the y values then x is the independent variable and y is the dependent variable and you should work out the least squares regression line (the line of best fit) of x on y given by

$$x = a' + b'y \quad \text{where} \quad b' = \frac{S_{xy}}{S_{yy}} = \frac{\sum(x_i - \bar{x})(y_i - \bar{y})}{\sum(y_i - \bar{y})^2} \quad \text{and} \quad a' = \bar{x} - b'\bar{y} \quad \text{you may use} \quad x - \bar{x} = b'(y - \bar{y})$$

$$S_{xy} = \sum(x_i - \bar{x})(y_i - \bar{y}) = \sum x_i y_i - \frac{(\sum x_i)(\sum y_i)}{n}$$

$$S_{yy} = \sum(y_i - \bar{y})^2 = \sum y_i^2 - \frac{(\sum y_i)^2}{n}$$

Note: None of these are given in your formula book. Just interchange x and y in the previous formulae.

Note this regression line also passes through $(\bar{x}, \bar{y})$

You can use the regression line to predict one value given the other. You should be wary about predicting values that are outside the region of given values as you do not know whether they follow the same pattern.

---

1. Find the regression line of y on x for the following data.
   $\sum x = 135$ $\sum y = 65$ $\sum x^2 = 3181$ $\sum y^2 = 787$ $\sum xy = 1561$ $n = 6$

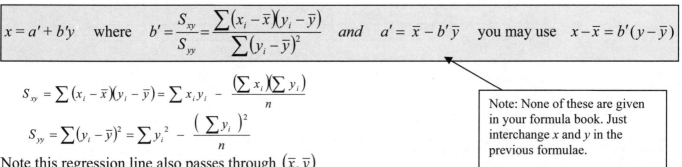

2. A financial manager records the number of lorry-loads of goods leaving his factory each week, together with the total production costs for those goods.

Lorry-loads (x)	10	13	17	14	16	5	8	4
Production costs (£100s) (y)	58	74	95	78	90	30	48	23

(a) Plot these points on a scatter diagram.
(b) Explain why this diagram would support the calculation of a regression line of y on x.
(c) Find an equation of the regression line of y on x in the form $y = a + bx$.
     (You may use $\Sigma x^2 = 1115$ and $\Sigma xy = 6315$)
(d) Interpret the slope b and the intercept a of your line.
(e) Find the expected production costs of 12 lorry-loads of goods.
(f) State, giving a reason, whether or not you would use the line to find the expected production costs of 30 lorry-loads.

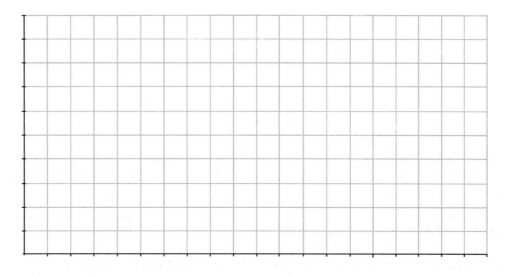

b)

c) $S_{xy} =$ $S_{xx} =$

     $\bar{x} =$ $\bar{y} =$

     $b = \dfrac{S_{xy}}{S_{xx}} =$ $a = \bar{y} - b\bar{x} =$

equation of the regression line of y on x is

d)

e)

f)

3. In the week before a maths test 10 students recorded the number of hours that they watched television. Their hours and test score are shown in the table

Test score	35	42	55	61	66	75	82	89	90	92
Hours	47	42	35	38	31	25	38	26	24	20

Use the appropriate regression line to estimate a value of test score for a student who watched 30 hours of television.

4. A gardener plants a large number of seedlings and measures a random sample of them throughout the year. He records the height of each seedling and the time since it was planted.

Time after planting in months (t)	2	3	4	5	6	7	8	9
Height of seedling in cm (h)	10	12.5	13.1	14.8	16	16.6	17	17.1

(a)　Calculate the equation of the least squares regression line in the form $h = a + bt$.
(b)　What does the gradient represent?
(c)　What does the intercept with the h axis represent?

5. Obtain the equation of the least squares regression line in the form $y = a + bx$ for n sets of data pairs (x,y) where:

$$n = 7 \quad \sum x = 645 \quad \sum x^2 = 64975 \quad \sum y = 45.77 \quad \sum y^2 = 303.53 \quad \sum xy = 4360.8$$

Using your calculator:
Enter the following as data items/lists and hence find required regression line either direct from your calculator or by obtaining Σx, Σy etc. and using the formulas.

6. A car rental firm records the age (to the nearest month) of a sample of its cars and the corresponding cost of servicing the cars over the past year.

A (age in months)	12	14	15	18	18	21	22	25
C (service costs in £)	45	100	60	85	100	90	115	120

Find the equation of the regression line of service cost on age.
Estimate the cost of servicing a 2 year old car.

7. Find the equation of the regression line of P on Q for the following set of data.

P	50	60	70	80	90	100	110	120	130	140
Q	5.6	4.8	4.7	4.2	3.9	3.5	3.0	2.6	2.5	2.1

8. Find the equations of the regression lines of y on x and x on y for the following set of data.

x	5	6	7	8	9	10
y	12	20	33	36	42	45

Use the appropriate regression line to estimate a value of y given $x = 8.5$

Mixed Questions

1. The 20 students on a Maths course recorded the time in minutes, x, to the nearest minute, spent travelling to college on a given day. The results are summarised here.

   $\sum x = 513 \quad \sum x^2 = 14971$

   Find the mean and standard deviation for this data.

2. The discrete random variable X has the following probability distribution.

x	0	1	2	3
$P(X = x)$	¼	k	k + ¼	2k

   (a) Find k
   (b) Calculate E (X) and Var(X)

3. This is the frequency diagram for a set of data on the number of correct answers obtained in a ten question quiz.

   (i) Describe two features of the distribution
   (ii) State the mode and find the value of the median
   (iii) Find the values of the upper and lower quartiles and hence draw a box-and-whisker diagram for the data
   (iv) Calculate the mean and the standard deviation of the data

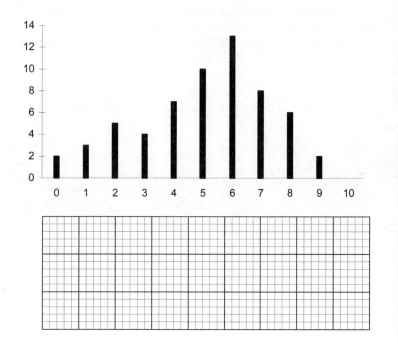

4. Debs is practising shooting at a goal. She decides to continue until she misses. The probability of her missing the goal is ¼. Assuming each shot is independent of other shots, find the probability that she first misses the goal
    a) on her 4th shot
    b) after her 4th shot
    c) before her 4th shot.

5. 75% of seeds from a supplier germinate when planted.
    (a) If 10 seeds are planted find the probability that
        (i) eight germinate
        (ii) eight or more germinate.
    (b) The seeds are packed in small packets of 10 seeds. If six packets are chosen at random find the probability that eight or more seeds germinate from all six packets.

6. Joe either goes to college by bus or he cycles. The probability that he cycles is 0.8. If he cycles the probability that he is late is 0.3 and if he goes by bus the probability that he is late is 0.4.
    a) Find the probability that on any particular day he is late.
    b) If on a particular day he was late , find the probability that he used the bus.

7. The table shows the time spent solving a mathematical puzzle, undertaken by 96 students

Time (secs) x	Number of students, f			
10-29	8			
30-39	7			
40-49	14			
50-59	23			
60-69	26			
70-79	12			
80-89	6			

(i) Calculate an estimate for the mean time taken to solve the puzzle. Explain why your answer is only an estimate.

(ii) Draw the cumulative frequency curve for this data.

(iii) Using your diagram, give estimates for the median and interquartile range.

(iv) Estimate how many students took longer than 75 seconds to solve the puzzle.

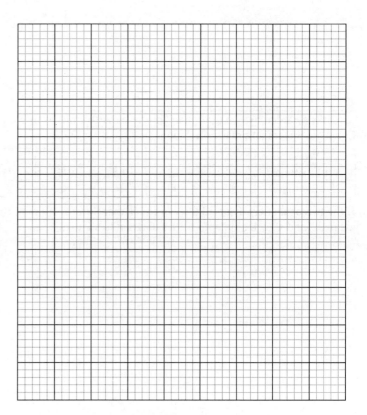

8. The weights of 200 small fish in one stretch of river were measured, and the following table of data was produced.

Weight (g)	50 -	100 -	200 -	300 -	400 -	600 -	700 -	900-1000
Number of fish	6	18	28	40	22	35	41	10

(i) Calculate an estimate for the mean weight of fish.

(ii) Calculate an estimate of the standard deviation.

9. Five cards are numbered 0, 1, 1, 2 and 3. If S is the random variable 'the value of the card when one is picked at random', find the expected score and the variance.

10. The marks awarded by two examiners for the same five pieces of work are shown in the table.

a) Calculate Spearman's rank correlation coefficient for the data.

Work	A	B	C	D	E
1st Examiner	48	83	65	92	71
2nd Examiner	65	90	36	86	57

b) If the two examiners assessed the work such that Spearman's rank correlation coefficient was +1 , what comment would you make and sketch a suitable scatter diagram to show this.

11. A biology student records the number of hours of sunshine, x, and the number of butterflies, y, seen in a garden for a sample of 10 days in June.

The data are summarised here:

$\sum x = 52.7$ $\sum x^2 = 318.59$ $\sum y = 124$ $\sum y^2 = 1778$ $\sum xy = 742.5$

(a) Find S_{xx}, S_{xy}, S_{yy}.
(b) Find the product moment correlation coefficient for these data.
(c) Explain why this value might support the fitting of a linear regression model of the form $y = a + bx$.
(d) Find the values of a and b (to three significant figures).
(e) Estimate the number of butterflies that might be seen on a day in June with 7 hours of sunshine.

NOW TRY SOME PAST PAPER QUESTIONS

Answers

Page4

1. $\bar{x} = \dfrac{3+5+7+9}{4} = 6$

$Var = \dfrac{9+25+49+81}{4} - 6^2 = 41 - 36 = 5$

$sd = \sqrt{5} = 2.24$ to 3 sig.fig

2. mean = 18.25   sd = 2.64338 = 2.64 to 3 sig.fig.
($\Sigma x = 365$, $\Sigma x^2 = 6801$)

Page5

3. $\bar{x} = \dfrac{\sum x}{n} = \dfrac{184}{20} = 9.2$

$var = \dfrac{\sum x^2}{n} - \bar{x}^2 = \dfrac{2648}{20} - 9.2^2 = 47.76$

$sd = \sqrt{47.76} = 6.91$ to 3 sig.fig

4. (i) $\sum h = 9 \times 12 = 108$,

$4 = \dfrac{\sum h^2}{n} - 144$

$\sum h^2 = 148 \times 9 = 1332$

(ii) $\bar{x} = \dfrac{108+2}{10} = 11$

$var = (1332 + 2^2)/10 - 11^2 = 12.6$

s.d. $= \sqrt{12.6} = 3.55$ to 3 sig.fig

5. a) mean = 6.775   sd = 1.09857 = 1.10 to 3 sig.fig
($\Sigma x = 27.1$, $\Sigma x^2 = 188.43$)
b) mean = 33.7   sd = 20.5526 = 20.6 to 3 sig.fig
($\Sigma x = 337$, $\Sigma x^2 = 15581$)
c) mean = 730.4   sd = 173.767 = 174 to 3 sig.fig
($\Sigma x = 3652$, $\Sigma x^2 = 2818000$)

Page6

1. The quickest swimmer took 14 seconds
2. The slowest swimmer took 22 seconds
3. The modal group is those students who took 16 or 17 seconds
4. The range of times for these swimmers is 8 seconds
5. The median time is 18 seconds

SQUASH PLAYERS
The mode = 36
The median = 32
Lower quartile = 23
Upper quartile = 40
Interquartile range = 17
Fairly symmetric

GOLF PLAYERS
The mode = 56
The median = 47
Lower quartile = 40
Upper quartile = 56
Interquartile range = 16
Negative skew.

Page7

1. mean, $\bar{x} = 15$
variance = 7.5
standard deviation, $sd_x = 2.7386$
mean, $\bar{z} = 5$
variance = 7.5
standard deviation, $sd_z = 2.7386$
the connection between.......
$\bar{z} = \bar{x} - 10$
$sd_z = sd_x$

2. i) $\bar{y} = 8.6 / 50 = 0.172$
then $\bar{x} = 0.172 + 35 = 35.172$
ii) var of $y = 112/50 - 0.172^2 = 2.210416$
sd of $y = 1.49 = $ sd of x
iii) $\Sigma x = 50 \times 35.172 = 1758.6$
iv) $2.210416 = \Sigma x^2 / 50 - 35.172^2$
$\Sigma x^2 = 61964$

Page8

3. $\bar{y} = 540 / 20 = 27$ then $\bar{x} = 27 + 180 = 207$
var of $y = 16025 / 20 - 27^2 = 72.25$
sd of $y = 8.5 = $ sd of x

4. $\bar{y} = 840 / 10 = 84$
then $\bar{x} = 84 + 400 = 484$
var of $y = 90810 / 10 - 84^2 = 2025$
sd of $y = 45 = $ sd of x

Page9

6, 7, 8, 9, 10, 10, 11, 11, 11, 12, 12, 12, 12, 12, 12, 13, 13, 13, 13, 15
Median $Q_2 = 12$ $Q_1 = 10$ $Q_3 = 12.5$
boxplot

1. $\Sigma x = 654$ $\bar{x} = 20.4375$ $\Sigma x^2 = 15246$
var = 58.74609   sd = 7.6646

```
0 | 5 7 9
1 | 0 2 4 4
1 | 5 5 6 6 6 7 8
2 | 0 0 2 3 3 3 4 4
2 | 5 6 6 7 8 9 9
3 | 1 2
3 | 8              2 | 5 means 25
```

median (at 16.5) is 21
$Q_1 = 15$ $Q_3 = 26$
boxplot

Page10

2. positive skew
$Q_1 = 32$ $Q_2 = 40$ $Q_3 = 52$
$\Sigma x = 1286$ $\bar{x} = 42.87$ $\Sigma x^2 = 62324$

$var = \dfrac{30}{29} \times 239.9156 = 248.189$ sd = 15.754

3. Mean of $x = 23 + 20 = 43$
sd of $x = 1.2$

4. Let $y = x - 15$
$\bar{y} = 4 / 20 = 0.2$
then $\bar{x} = 0.2 + 15 = 15.2$
var of $y = 1.448 / 20 - 0.2^2 = 0.0324$
sd of $y = 0.18 = $ sd of x

5. (i) Positive skew (ii) (a) 22.5
(b) 27.5 - 17.5 = 10
(c) 18

Page 11

mark, x	f	fx	x^2	fx^2
0	1	0×1=0	$0^2=0$	0×1=0
1	2	1×2=2	$1^2=1$	1×2=2
2	2	2×2=4	$2^2=4$	4×2=8
3	3	9	9	27
4	6	24	16	96
5	9	45	$5^2=25$	225
6	12	72	36	432
7	7	49	49	343
8	5	40	64	320
9	2	18	81	162
10	1	10	100	100

$\sum f = 50$ $\sum fx = 273$ $\sum fx^2 = 1715$

Mean, $= \dfrac{273}{50} = 5.46$

$Variance = \dfrac{1715}{50} - 5.46^2 = 4.4884$

Standard deviation, sd $= \sqrt{4.4884} = 2.11858 = 2.12$ to 3 sig.fig

Page12

1.

mark	freq			
9	5	45	81	405
10	9	90	100	900
11	12	132	121	1452
12	6	72	144	864
13	2	26	169	338

Mean = 365 / 32 = 10.735294 = 10.7 to 3 sig.fig

$Variance = \dfrac{3959}{34} - 10.735294^2 = 1.189584$

sd $= \sqrt{1.189584} = 1.09068 = 1.09$ to 3 sig.fig

2. $\bar{x} = \dfrac{\sum fx}{\sum f} = \dfrac{116}{29} = 4$

$Variance = \dfrac{498}{29} - 4^2 = 1.172413793$

sd $= \sqrt{1.172413793} = 1.08278$

Page 13

3. a) mean = 8.22641 = 8.23 to 3 sig.fig.
sd = 1.6211 = 1.62 to 3 sig.fig.
($\Sigma x = 436$, $\Sigma x^2 = 3726$)
b) mean = 1.30612 = 1.31 to 3 sig.fig.
sd = 0.97319 = 0.937 to 3 sig.fig.
($\Sigma x = 64$, $\Sigma x^2 = 130$)
c) mean = 3.3
sd = 2.41039 = 2.41 to 3 sig.fig.
($\Sigma x = 132$, $\Sigma x^2 = 668$)

Height	freq	class width	freq density
5-14	10	10	10 ÷ 10 = 1
15-19	12	5	12 ÷ 5 = 1.2
20-24	20	5	4
25-29	18	5	3.6
30-34	12	5	2.4
35-39	6	5	1.2
40-44	4	5	0.8
45-54	4	10	0.4

Page14

Height	f	x	fx	x^2	fx^2
5-14	10	9.5	95	90.25	902.5
15-19	12	17	204	289	3468
20-24	20	22	440	484	9680
25-29	18	27	486	729	13122
30-34	12	32	384	1024	12288
35-39	6	37	222	1369	8214
40-44	4	42	168	1764	7056
45-54	4	49.5	198	2450.25	9801

$\sum f = 86$ $\sum fx = 2197$ $\sum fx^2 = 64531.5$

$\bar{x} = \dfrac{\sum fx}{\sum f} = \dfrac{2197}{86} = 25.5465$

$Var = \dfrac{64531.5}{86} - 25.5465^2 = 97.742$

sd $= \sqrt{97.742} = 9.886456 = 9.89$ to 3 sig.fig

1.

f	x	fx	x^2	fx^2
2	74.5	149	5550.25	11100.5
5	124.5	622.5	15500.25	77501.25
15	174.5	2617.5	30450.25	456753.8
11	224.5	2469.5	50400.25	554402.8
6	274.5	1647	75350.25	452101.5
39		7505.5		1551860

mean 192.4487 = 192 to 3 sig.fig
variance = 2754.77   standard deviation = 52.5

2. mid class values 14.5, 24.5, 34.5, 44.5, 55.5
mean = 34.9375 = 34.9 to 3 sig.fig.
sd = 9.67579 = 9.68 to 3 sig.fig.
($\Sigma x = 2795$, $\Sigma x^2 = 105140$)

Page15

3. $\Sigma f = 40$ $\Sigma fx = 66.95$ $\Sigma fx^2 = 112.3575$
mean 1.67   sd 0.0866 to 3 sig.fig

Example

time(sec)	Frequency	C frequency
20-29	3	3
30-39	14	17
40-49	25	42
50-59	30	72
60-69	18	90
70-79	9	99
80-89	1	100

Answers are approximate
Median = 53
Lower Quartile = 43
Upper Quartile = 61
IQR = 61 - 43 = 18

Page16

1.

freq	width	freq/width
10	20	0.5
12	5	2.4
18	5	3.6
10	10	1

2. $\Sigma f = 32$ $\Sigma fx^2 = 374$ $\Sigma fx^2 = 4406$

Mean = 374 / 32 = 11.6875

Variance = $4406 / 32 - 11.6875^2 = 1.0898$

Standard deviation = 1.04 to 3 sig.fig.

3. Answers are approximate

Median = 18min

$Q_1 = 15$ $Q_3 = 21$ IQR = 21 - 15 = 6 min

Page17

4. . Let $y = x - 30$

$\bar{y} = 320 / 40 = 8$ then $\bar{x} = 8 + 30 = 38$

var of $y = 2920 / 40 - 8^2 = 9$

sd of y = 3 = sd of x

5.

x	fx	x^2	fx^2
1.5	3	2.25	4.5
4.5	22.5	20.25	101.25
7.5	90	56.25	675
10.5	84	110.25	882
13.5	121.5	182.25	1640.25
17.5	17.5	306.25	306.25
30	90	900	2700
totals	428.5		6309.25

mean £10.71   sd £6.56   median £10

$Q_1 = 7$ $Q_3 = 13$ IQR = 13 - 7 = 6

Page19

1. (a) 26/52 = ½   (b) 13/52 = ¼

(c) 4/52 = 1/13   (d) 1/13 + 1/13 = 2/13

2. (a) P(H and 2) = ½ × ¼ = ⅛

(b) P(H and even) = ½ × ½ = ¼

3. (a) ¾   (b) ¼ × ⅓ = 1/12

4.   HHH HHT HTH HTT

THH THT TTH TTT

(a) ⅛   (b) ⅞ (c) ⅜

5. (a) 36   (b) P(18) = 2/36 = 1/18

(c) P(4) = 3/36 = 1/12   (d) P(odd) = 9/36 = ¼

(e) P(even) = 27/18 = ¾

6. (a) P(H and 6) = 1/12

(b) P(T and odd) = 3/12 = ¼

Page21

1. (a) 0.6 × 0.9 = 0.54

(b) 0.6 × 0.1 + 0.4 × 0.2 = 0.06 + 0.08 = 0.14

2. (ii) $\frac{3}{5} \times \frac{4}{5} \times \frac{4}{5} = \frac{48}{125}$

(iii) $\frac{3}{5} \times \frac{1}{5} \times \frac{1}{5} + \frac{2}{5} \times \frac{1}{5} \times \frac{4}{5} = \frac{3}{125} + \frac{8}{125} = \frac{11}{125}$

3. (i) 0.6 × 0.7 = 0.42

(ii) 0.42 + 0.4 × 0.8 = 0.74

(iii) $\frac{0.42}{0.74} = \frac{21}{37}$

Page22

1. $1 - P(\text{no sixes}) = 1 - (5/6)^3 = 0.421296$

2. (i)1/36 + 1/36 + 1/36 = 3/36 = 1/12

(ii)P(9and12)+P(10and11)+.....

$=1/36 \times 1/36 + 1/36 \times 1/36+...$

= 10/36² = 10/216 = 5/648

(iii) 1/6 × 1/6 + 1/6 × 1/6 +...

......+ 1/36 × 1/36 + 1/36 × 1/36...

= $5/6^2 + 6/36^2 = 31/216$

3. (a) 0.7 × 0.35 + 0.3 × 0.15 = 0.29

(b) $P(W|L) = P(W \cap L)/P(L)$

= 0.7 × 0.35/0.29 = 0.8448

(c) 0.7 × 0.65 / (1 - 0.29) = 0.6408

Page23

4 × 3 × 2 × 1 = 24

3 × 3 × 3 × 3 × 3 = 243

Page24

1. 8 × 7 × 6 × 5 × 4 × 3 × 2 × 1 = 40320

2. 8 × 7 × 6 × 5 × 4 = 6720

3. (a) 7! = 5040   (b) 7 × 6 × 5 × 4 = 840

4. 7! = 5040

5. (a) $^4P_3 = 4! / 1! = 24$ numbers

(b) 4×4×4 = 64 numbers

(c) Numbers beginning with 4 or 5 will be too big

So choice for first number is 2 or 3

2×4×4 = 32 numbers

Page25

6. $^5C_3 = 5!/(3!2!) = 10$ $^7C_3 = 7!/(3!4!) = 35$

$^5C_3 \times ^7C_3 = 10 \times 35 = 350$

7. $^8C_4 \times ^6C_5 = 8!/(4!4!) \times 6!/(5!1!) = 70 \times 6 = 420$

1. $^7C_4 \times ^7C_5 = 7!/(4!3!) \times 7!/(2!5!) = 35 \times 21 = 735$

$^6C_3 \times ^7C_5 = 6!/(3!3!) \times 21 = 20 \times 21 = 420$

Mrs B on (and Mr A) $^6C_4 \times ^5C_3 = 15 \times 10 = 150$

Mr C on (and Mr A) $^5C_2 \times ^6C_5 = 10 \times 6 = 60$

MrA and notMrs B not Mr C

$^5C_3 \times ^6C_5 = 10 \times 6 = 60$

Total 270

Page26

2. a) $^3C_1 \times ^5C_2 \times ^8C_4 = 3 \times 10 \times 70 = 2100$

b) $^8C_5 = 56$

c) last 5 on coach $^{16}C_5 = 4368$

56/4368 = 1/78

3. 3 women (&3men) $^6C_3 \times ^5C_3 = 20 \times 10 = 200$

4 women (&2men) $^6C_4 \times ^5C_2 = 15 \times 10 = 150$

5 women (&1man) $^6C_5 \times ^5C_1 = 6 \times 5 = 30$

6 women   1

Total 381

4.(a) 5! = 120

(b) boys together (2 ways) 4! × 2 = 48

Not sitting together 120 - 48 = 72

P(not sit together) 72/120 = 3/5

5. $^{20}C_{11} = 167960$ $^{19}C_{10} = 92378$

P(goalkeeper picked) = 92378/167960 = 11/20

6. 4! = 24

first digit 4 * * 2   last must be 2

1×2×1×1 = 2possibilities

first digit 5 * * *   last digit must be 2or4

1×2×1×2 = 4

total of 6possibilities

P(even and >4000) = 6/24 = ¼

Page27

1.   0   1   2   3

$\frac{1}{8}$ $\frac{3}{8}$ $\frac{3}{8}$ $\frac{1}{8}$

$E(H) = 0 \times \frac{1}{8} + 1 \times \frac{3}{8} + 2 \times \frac{3}{8} + 3 \times \frac{1}{8} = 1.5$

$E(H^2) = 0 \times \frac{1}{8} + 1^2 \times \frac{3}{8} + 2^2 \times \frac{3}{8} + 3^2 \times \frac{1}{8} = 3$

$Var(H) = 3 - 1.5^2 = 0.75$

2.   1   2   3   4

0.1 0.2 0.3 0.4

$E(S) = 1 \times 0.1 + 2 \times 0.2 + 3 \times 0.3 + 4 \times 0.4 = 3$

$E(S^2) = 1^2 \times 0.1 + 2^2 \times 0.2 + 3^2 \times 0.3 + 4^2 \times 0.4 = 10$

$Var(S) = 10 - 3^2 = 1$

Page28

3. x 1   2   3   4   5

P(X=x) 4/50 7/50 10/50 13/50 16/50

E(X) = 180/50 = 3.6 $E(X^2) = 730/50 = 14.6$

$Var(X) = 14.6 - 3.6^2 = 1.64$

4.   3   5   7   9

¼   ¼   ¼   ¼

$E(S) = 3 \times ¼ + 5 \times ¼ + 7 \times ¼ + 9 \times ¼ = 24/4 = 6$

$E(S^2) = = 9 \times ¼ + 25 \times ¼ + 49 \times ¼ + 81 \times ¼ = 41$

$Var(S) = 41 - 36 = 5$

5. a)   1   3   5   6

1/6   1/3   1/6   1/3

b) $E(X) = 1 \times 1/6 + 3 \times 1/3 + 5 \times 1/6 + 6 \times 1/3 = 4$

$Var(X) = 1 \times 1/6 + 9 \times 1/3 + 25 \times 1/6 + 36 \times 1/3 - 4^2$

= 10/3

Page29

SFFSF   SFFFS   FSSFF   FSFSF

FSFFS   FFSSF   FFSFS   FFFSS

P(three sixes from 5 throws) = $^5C_3 \left(\frac{1}{6}\right)^3 \left(\frac{5}{6}\right)^2$

P(four sixes from 5 throws) = $^5C_4 \left(\frac{1}{6}\right)^4 \left(\frac{5}{6}\right)^1$

P(five sixes from 5 throws) = $^5C_5 \left(\frac{1}{6}\right)^5 = \left(\frac{1}{6}\right)^5$

Page30

1. (c) $P(X = 0) = (4/5)^6 = 0.262144$

P(X = 1) = 0.393216

$P(X = 2) = ^6C_2(1/5)^2(4/5)^4 = 15 \times 0.04 \times 0.4096$

= 0.24576

$P(X \geq 3) = 1 - [0.262144 + 0.393216 + 0.24576]$

= 1 - 0.90112 = 0.09888

d) Mean = n × p = 20 × 1/5 = 4

Variance = $\sigma^2 = n \times p \times q = 20 \times 1/5 \times 4/5 = 3.2$

Standard deviation, $\sigma = \sqrt{3.2} = 1.79$ to 3 sig.fig.

Page31

2. X = score out of ten

$X \sim B(10, ¼)$

(a) $P(X = 0) = (¾)^{10} = 0.0563$

(b) $P(X = 1) = ^{10}C_1(¼)^1(¾)^9 = 0.1877$

(c) P(X < 3) = P(X = 0) + P(X = 1) + P(X = 2)

$P(X = 2) = ^{10}C_2(¼)^2(¾)^8 = 0.28157$

P(X < 3) = 0.0563 + 0.1877 + 0.28157 = 0.5256

(d) $P(X \geq 5) = 1 - P(X < 5)$

$P(X = 4) = ^{10}C_4(¼)^4(¾)^6 = 0.145998$

$P(X = 3) = ^{10}C_3(¼)^3(¾)^7 = 0.250282$

$P(X \geq 5) = 1 - (0.5256 + 0.250282 + 0.145998)$

= 0.078

Mean = n × p = 10 × ¼ = 2.5

Variance = $\sigma^2 = n \times p \times q = 20 \times ¼ \times ¾ = 1.875$

Standard dev, $\sigma = \sqrt{1.875} = 1.37$ to 3 sig.fig.

3. X = number of twos

$X \sim B(8, 1/3)$

(a) $P(X = 6) = ^8C_6(1/3)^6(2/3)^2 = 0.0170705685$

(b) $P(X = 7) = ^8C_7(1/3)^7(2/3)^1 = 0.00243865264$

$P(X = 8) = (1/3)^8 = 0.00015241579$

P(X > 5) = 0.01966

Page32

1. P(X≤6) = 0.9629

P(X≤7) = 0.9887

P(X=7) = 0.0258

P(X=4) = 0.7687 - 0.5665 = 0.2022

P(X<3) = P(X≤2) = 0.3287

P(X>8) = 1 - 0.9972 = 0.0028

2. P(Y≤10) = 0.0480

P(Y≤17) = 0.9645

P(Y=12) = 0.2277 - 0.1133 = 0.1144

P(Y=18) = 0.9924 - 0.9645 = 0.0279

P(Y<16) = P(Y≤15) = 0.7625

P(Y>16) = 1 - P(Y≤16) = 1 - 0.8929 = 0.1071

P(Y≥14) = 1 - P(Y≤13) = 1 - 0.3920 = 0.6080

Page33

3. a) X = the number of red sweets

$X \sim B(20, ⅔)$

$P(X \geq 15) = 1 - P(Y \leq 14) = 1 - 0.7028 = 0.2972$

b) Y = the number of packets containing at least 15 red sweets

$Y \sim B(5, 0.2972)$

$P(Y \geq 3) = 1 - P(Y \leq 2)$

$P(Y = 0) = (1 - 0.2972)^5 = 0.7028^5 = 0.171458$

$P(Y = 1) = 5 \times 0.2972^1 0.7028^4 = 0.362532$

$P(Y = 2) = 10 \times 0.2972^2 0.7028^3 = 0.306615$

$P(Y \geq 3) = 1 - 0.840605 = 0.1594$

1. (i) 0.3154 (ii) 0.2322

2. (i) $6 \times 0.225^5 0.775^1 = 0.00268$

(ii) $0.00268 + 0.225^6 = 0.002811$

3. (i) 0.7759 (ii) 0.2503

4. $P(X = 0) = (5/8)^6 = 0.0596046447$

$P(X = 1) = 6 \times (3/8)^1 \times (5/8)^5 = 0.2145767212$

(i) P(X < 2) = P(X = 0) + P(X = 1) = 0.27418

(ii) $P(X = 2) = 15 \times (3/8)^2 \times (5/8)^4 = 0.3218650818$

P(X≤2) = 0.321865 + 0.27418 = 0.5960

5. P(X≥6) = 1 - P(X≤5) = 1 - 0.2703 = 0.7297

6. 11 (from tables)

Page34

7. P(X = 0) = 0.5787

P(X = 1) = 0.3472

P(X = 2) = 0.0695

P(X = 3) = 0.0046

8. P(X≥4) = 1 - P(X≤3) = 1 - 0.6563 = 0.3437

9. P(X≥3) = 1 - P(X≤2) = 1 - 0.9645 = 0.0355

10.(i) P(X = 3) = 0.0574 (ii) P(X≤2) = 0.9298

11.(i) P(X = 4) = 0.2322 (ii) P(X≤2) = 0.5941

(iii) P(X>6) = 1 - P(X≤6) = 1 - 0.9915 = 0.0085

Page35

12. (i) P(X = 10) = 0.1074

(ii) P(X≥8) = 1 - P(X≤7) = 1 - 0.3222 = 0.6778

(iii) P(X<5) = P(X≤4) = 0.0064

13.(i) P(X<2) = P(X≤1) = 0.1756

(ii) P(X = 5) = 0.1029

(iii) P(X<5) = P(X≤4) = 0.8298

(iv) P(X>5) = 1 - P(X≤5) = 1 - 0.9327 = 0.0673

(v) P(X≥5) = 1 - P(X≤4) = 1 - 0.8298 = 0.1702

14 (i) 2/5 = 0.4 (ii) B(10,0.4)   P(X≤3) = 0.3823

Page36

1. $P(X = 1) = ¼$ $P(X = 2) = ¾ × ¼ = 3/16$
$P(X = 3) = ¾ × ¾ × ¼ = 9/64$
$P(X = 4) = ¾ × ¾ × ¾ × ¼ = 27/256$
$P(X ≥ 3) = ¾ × ¾ = 9/16$
$P(X > 3) = ¾ × ¾ × ¾ = 27/64$
$P(X ≤ 3) = 1 - 27/64 = 37/64$

2. $P(Y = 2) = 0.3 × 0.7 = 0.21$
$P(Y = 3) = 0.3 × 0.3 × 0.7 = 0.063$
$P(Y = 2 \text{ or } 3) = 0.21 + 0.063 = 0.273$
$P(Y ≤ 5) = 1 - 0.3^5 = 0.99757$

Page37

3. X = the number of throws up to and including the first 'pin up'

$X \sim \text{Geo}(\frac{2}{5})$

a) (i) $P(X = 3) = \frac{3}{5} × \frac{3}{5} × \frac{2}{5} = \frac{18}{125}$

(ii) $P(X = 5) = \frac{3}{5} × \frac{3}{5} × \frac{3}{5} × \frac{3}{5} × \frac{2}{5} = \frac{162}{3125}$

b) $P(X > 6) = \left(\frac{3}{5}\right)^6 = \frac{729}{15625}$

c) $P(X < 5) = P(X ≤ 4) = 1 - \left(\frac{3}{5}\right)^4 = \frac{554}{625}$

4. a) (i) $P(X = 2) = 0.8 × 0.2 = 0.16$
(ii) $P(X = 5) = 0.8 × 0.8 × 0.8 × 0.8 × 0.2$
$= 0.08192$
b) $P(X > 6) = 0.8^6 = 0.262144$
c) $P(X < 3) = P(X ≤ 2) = 1 - 0.8^2 = 0.36$

5. i) $X \sim \text{Geo}\left(\frac{1}{5}\right)$

ii) $P(X = 3) = \frac{4}{5} × \frac{4}{5} × \frac{1}{5} = \frac{16}{125}$

iii) $P(X < 4) = P(X ≤ 3) = 1 - \left(\frac{4}{5}\right)^3 = \frac{61}{125}$

iv) $E(X) = \frac{1}{\frac{1}{5}} = 5$

6. i) $P(Y = 5) = 0.9^4 × 0.1 = 0.06561$
ii) $P(3 ≤ Y < 5) = P(X = 3) + P(X = 4)$
$= 0.9^2 × 0.1 + 0.9^3 × 0.1$
$= 0.1539$

iii) $E(X) = \frac{1}{0.1} = 10$

Page38

1.

484	196	-308
64	9	-24
1	16	-4
169	121	-143
324	100	-180
TOTALS 1042	442	-659

$r = \frac{-659}{\sqrt{1042 × 412}} = -0.971047$

Very strong negative correlation.

Page39

2.

$r = \dfrac{324 - \frac{71 × 38}{6}}{\sqrt{\left(1127 - \frac{71^2}{6}\right)}\sqrt{\left(332 - \frac{38^2}{6}\right)}}$

$= \dfrac{-125.6666}{\sqrt{(286.8333 × 91.3333)}}$

$= \dfrac{-125.6666....}{161.8562462} = -0.7764091256$

$= -0.776$ (3 d.p.)

A fair negative correlation between the two variables.

3. $\sum x = 698$ $\sum y = 1667$ $\sum x^2 = 49378$
$\sum y^2 = 278467$ $\sum xy = 116934$

$S_{xy} = 116934 - \frac{698 × 1667}{10} = 577.4$

$S_{xx} = 49378 - \frac{698^2}{10} = 657.6$

$S_{yy} = 278467 - \frac{1667^2}{10} = 578.1$

$r = \frac{577.4}{\sqrt{657.6 × 578.1}} = 0.936$

A strong positive correlation between height and weight

Page40

4. a) A strong positive correlation between the two variables.
b) A strong negative correlation between the two variables.
c) A weak positive correlation between the two variables – certainly not worth considering as significant.
d) A weak negative correlation between the two variables – certainly not worth considering as significant.
e) A fair positive correlation between the two variables.
f) A fair negative correlation between the two variables.

5. a) $S_{xy} = 98.5$
$S_{xx} = 143.5$
$S_{yy} = 82.83333...$
$r = 0.903457... = 0.903$ (3 d.p.)
b) $r = 0.8159488.. = 0.816$ (3 d.p.)
c) $r = -0.779$ (3 d.p.)

6. a) $S_{xy} = -1182.5$
$S_{xx} = 269.5$
$S_{yy} = 5335.5..$
$r = -0.98613 = -0.986$ (3 d.p.)
b) $r = 0.435$ (3 d.p.)

7. $r = 0.79443 = 0.794$ (3 d.p.)

8. $r = -0.993$ (3 d.p.)

9. $r = 0.972$ (3 d.p.)

Page41

1. $\sum d^2 = 12$

$r_s = 1 - \frac{6 × 12}{6 × 35} = 0.657$ fair agreement

2. $\sum d^2 = 16$

$r_s = 1 - \frac{6 × 16}{5 × 24} = 0.2$ weak agreement

3. $\sum d^2 = 26$

$r_s = 1 - \frac{6 × 26}{10 × 99} = 0.842$ fairly good agreement

Page42

1. $\overline{x} = 22.5$ $\overline{y} = 10.8333...$

$S_{xy} = 98.5$
$S_{xx} = 143.5$
$b = 98.5 / 143.5 = 0.68641$
$a = 10.83333 - 0.68641 × 22.5 = -4.6109$
$y = -4.61 + 0.686 x$ using 3 sig.fig.

Page43

2.a) Scatter diagram
b) The data appears linear. There are a fixed number of points.
c) To 3 d.p. $y = 2.691 + 5.454x$
d) The slope gives an estimate of the increase in production costs for one extra lorry-load. The intercept gives an estimate of the production costs when no lorry-loads leave the factory: that is when no goods have been produced, so these costs are just overhead costs.
e) $Y = 2.691 + 5.454 × 12 = 68.139$ So costs are estimated to be 68.139 × £100. Say about £6800.
f) No–extrapolation is not reliable. 30 is outside the range of given values.

3. If test score is x and Hours is y then you require x on y
$\overline{x} = 68.7$ $\overline{y} = 32.6$
$S_{xy} = -1393.2$
$S_{yy} = 696.4$
$b = -1393.2 / 696.4 = -2.000574$
$a = 68.7 - -2.000574 × 32.6 = 139.9187$
$x = 140 - 2.00 y$ using 3 sig.fig.
$y = 30, x = 80$

Page44

4. $\sum t = 44$ $\sum t^2 = 284$ $\sum h = 117.1$ $\sum th = 686$
$b = 0.9988.... $ $a = 9.1440$
$h = 9.14 + 0.999t$ using 3 sig.fig.
b) Increase in height per unit of time.
c) Height when planted

5. $\overline{y} = 6.5386$ $\overline{x} = 92.1429$
$S_{xy} = 143.42$ $S_{xx} = 5542.86$
$b = 0.025875$ $a = 4.1544$
$y = 4.15 + 0.026x$ using 3 sig.fig.

6. $C = 4.62928 + 4.67562 A$ and using 3 sig.fig.
$C = 4.63 + 4.68 A$
$A = 24$, $C = 116.84$

7. $P = 191.695 - 26.2047 Q$ and using 3 sig.fig.
$P = 192 - 26.2 Q$

8. y on x
$y = -18.8095 + 6.68571 x$ and using 3 sig.fig.
$y = -18.8 + 6.69 x$
x on y
$x = 3.06889 + 0.14141y$ and using 3 sig.fig.
$x = 3.07 + 0.141y$
Using y on x
$x = 8.5, y = 38$ to 2 sig.fig.

Page45 Mixed questions

1. Mean = 25.65 standard deviation = 9.52

2. a) Total probability = 1
$¼ + k + k + ¼ + 2k = 1$
$4k = ½$
$k = \frac{1}{8}$

b) $E(X) = 0 × \frac{1}{4} + 1 × \frac{1}{8} + 2 × \frac{3}{8} + 3 × \frac{1}{4} = \frac{13}{8}$

$E(X^2) = 0 × \frac{1}{4} + 1 × \frac{1}{8} + 4 × \frac{3}{8} + 9 × \frac{1}{4} = \frac{31}{8}$

$\text{Var}(X) = \frac{31}{8} - \left(\frac{13}{8}\right)^2 = 1.23$

3.(i) Discrete data, negatively skewed.
(ii) mode 6, median 5
(iii) lq = 4, uq = 7
(iv) $\overline{x} = 303/60 = 5.05$

s.d. $= \sqrt{\frac{1827}{60} - 5.05^2} = 2.2242976 = 2.22$

Page46

4. a) $¾ × ¾ × ¾ × ¼ = 27/256$
b) $(¾)^4 = 81/256$
c) $1 - (¾)^3 = 1 - 27/64 = 37/64$

5. a) X = Number of seeds that germinate
$X \sim \text{B}(10, 0.75)$
(i) $P(X=8) = {}^{10}C_8 (0.75)^8 (0.25)^2 = 0.28156$
(ii) $P(X ≥ 8) = 0.28156 + 0.1877 + 0.05631$
$= 0.5256$
b) $(0.5256)^6 = 0.0211$

6. a) P(late) = 0.32 b) 0.08/0.32 = 0.25

Page47

7. (i) using midpoints 19.5, 34.5, 44.5, etc
$\overline{x} = 5352/96 = 55.75$
Estimate because we do not know the actual values
(ii)cum freq 8, 15, 29, 52, 78, 90, 96
plot at 29.5, 39.5, etc
(iii) Approx answers median 58, lq = 46 uq = 67
IQR = 67 - 46 = 21
(iv) 96 - 85 = 11

Page48

8. (i) $\overline{x} = 100200/200 = 501$

(ii) s.d. $= \sqrt{\frac{62641250}{200} - 501^2}$
$= 249.4098 = 249$

9.

0	1	2	3
$\frac{1}{5}$	$\frac{2}{5}$	$\frac{1}{5}$	$\frac{1}{5}$

$E(X) = 0 × \frac{1}{5} + 1 × \frac{2}{5} + 2 × \frac{1}{5} + 3 × \frac{1}{5} = 1.4$

$E(X^2) = 0 × \frac{1}{5} + 1^2 × \frac{2}{5} + 2^2 × \frac{1}{5} + 3^2 × \frac{1}{5} = 3$

$\text{Var}(X) = 3 - 1.4^2 = 1.04$

10. a) d = 2 1 1 1 1
$\sum d^2 = 4 + 1 + 1 + 1 + 1$
$r_s = 1 - (6 × 8/5 × 24) = 0.6$
b) In complete agreement *of the order* of merit of the work
Any graph which shows y increasing as x increases.

Page49

11. a) $S_{xx} = 318.59 - 52.7^2 / 10 = 40.861$
$S_{xy} = 742.5 - 57.2 × 124 / 10 = 89.02$
$S_{yy} = 1778 - 124^2 / 10 = 240.4$

b) pmcc $= \frac{89.02}{\sqrt{40.861 × 240.4}} = 0.898185$
$= 0.898$ (to 3s.f.)

c) positive correlation close to 1.
d) b = 89.02 / 40.861 = 2.1786055 = 2.18
$a = 12.4 - 2.1786.55 × 5.27 = 0.9187489 = 0.919$
e) $y = 0.919 + 2.18 × 7 = 16.179$ say 16 butterflies.